Recalling the Medical Officer of Health

Recalling the Medical Officer of Health

Writings by Sidney Chave

EDITED BY
MICHAEL WARREN AND HUW FRANCIS

King Edward's Hospital Fund for London

© King Edward's Hospital Fund for London 1987
Printed in England by Hollen Street Press
Distributed for the King's Fund by Oxford University Press

ISBN 0 19 724643 5

King's Fund Publishing Office
2 St Andrew's Place
London NW1 4LB

Dedicated to Sidney's wife Eileen
and their children Jillian and Jeremy

Sidney Chave began his career in 1929 when at the age of 15 he became a laboratory boy at the newly opened London School of Hygiene and Tropical Medicine. He retired in 1979 as Emeritus Senior Lecturer in Public Health. The knowledge and enthusiasm he imparted through his lectures have made a lasting contribution to the history of public health. He died in 1985.

Foreword

Sidney Chave was part of the great public health tradition. His work over more than fifty years at the London School of Hygiene and Tropical Medicine involved him intimately in the development of the public health field and his clarity of presentation was a model.

When he died Sidney was working on a book on the rise and fall of the medical officer of health. This is a topic of great current interest because of the mounting awareness of health by the people of this country and the enquiry into the public health function led by the chief medical officer, Sir Donald Acheson.

The contribution of the medical officer of health to the development of public health has tended to be forgotten with the changes that have taken place since the abolition of the post in 1974. However, the subsequent development of a new form of community medicine is not widely understood and there is still considerable uncertainty regarding the wide-ranging role of the community physician in contrast to the clearly defined role of the medical officer of health.

In this volume Professor Michael Warren and Dr Huw Francis have collected some of Sidney Chave's important works and, in order to relate them to current practice, Dr Francis has added an epilogue.

Sidney Chave will be remembered especially by the many colleagues and students who had the good fortune to meet him and become his friends. It is in the context of his devotion to the subject and the need for our understanding of it that I commend this volume.

Patrick J S Hamilton
1987

Contents

Preface

When Sidney Chave died on 11 February 1985 from a cruel illness which he had characteristically borne with fortitude and hope, he was writing a book on the history of the medical officer of health. It began with the appointment of the first doctor to hold that post, Dr WH Duncan, and was intended to finish at the time of the abolition of the post in local government in 1974. Unfortunately Dr Chave did not get beyond completing a first draft of the earlier chapters and of sections of the later chapters. As it is not possible or desirable to attempt to copy his style or to tell the story as he would have done, the completed book cannot be produced. However, his contributions to the history of public health, and of the medical officer of health in particular, are of lasting value, so some of these have been brought together in the current volume.

Dr Chave had given a special lecture on the appointment and work of Dr Duncan, and this is reproduced as the first chapter. The next chapter has been taken from the draft of the book already mentioned; it outlines the first appointments of medical officers of health in London and presents material not previously published. This is followed by two papers written by Dr Chave about that famous event in the history of epidemiology, the outbreak of cholera in Broad Street in 1854. Dr John Snow's name is forever associated with the investigation of this epidemic, but the subsequent actions of the medical officer of health, Dr Edwin Lankester, are not so well-known, nor are the important confirmatory investigations of the curate, the Rev Henry Whitehead. These two chapters convey something of the frustrations experienced and the perseverence required by the pioneers in public health. Chapter 5 is taken from the draft of the book; it sets out the rapid development of public health in the second half of the 19th century, and describes the founding of the Society of Medical Officers of Health and the launching of its journal *Public Health*. The final contribution written by Dr Chave is the text of the Monckton Copeman Lecture (Chapter 6), and forms a summary of the book he was engaged upon. This chapter sets out, in his characteristic way, his view of the rise and fall of the medical officer of health; it recapitulates some points made in chapters 2 and 5 and takes the story on to 1974. Huw Francis has contributed an important epilogue bringing the account up to date. The book concludes with an annotated bibliography of the history of public health compiled by Dorothy Watkins followed by appendices listing holders of major offices related to public health and a list of Dr Chave's publications.

The editors are grateful to Professor Patrick Hamilton for his help in producing this book.

Michael Warren
Huw Francis
1987

Prologue

An appreciation of Sidney Chave

Sidney Chave was a remarkable man. He was born in 1914, and, after the death of his father in France in 1917, Sidney was brought up by his widowed mother. He joined the staff of the London School of Hygiene and Tropical Medicine as a laboratory boy in the Department of Chemistry as Applied to Hygiene in 1929, the year in which the School was formally opened by the Prince of Wales. During the 1939–45 war, Sidney was seconded to the (Emergency) Public Health Laboratory Service, working for a time at Oxford, and then back at the School in London. During this time he kept a detailed diary of both his home life and his work at the School; a copy of this diary is now lodged at the Imperial War Museum. In 1946 he returned to the School's staff and was promoted to Senior Technician. During the next few years he studied at Birkbeck College, and in 1951 obtained an honours degree in psychology from London University.

In 1952 Sidney Chave was appointed to the academic staff in the Department of Public Health. His teaching and tutoring skills quickly became apparent, his lectures being noted for their lucidity. At first he lectured on aspects of water supplies, purification and sewage disposal, and to these he later added introductory lectures on radiation. He had always been interested in the history of public health, about which he published papers (some included in this volume) and lectured. During the 1950s he developed an interest in and knowledge of health education and this became one of his major concerns. For his doctorate of philosophy, Sidney carried out an important study of mental health in the new town of Harlow; a report of this study, written in conjunction with Lord Taylor, was published as a book in 1964 and has remained one of the major contributions to the subject.

In 1969, Sidney became a senior lecturer in the Department of Community Health (previously Public Health), directed by Professor JN Morris CBE. In a tribute to Sidney, Professor Morris wrote in the 'Report on the School's Work' for 1984–5:

'When I came to the School to develop teaching for emergent Community Medicine, he [Sidney] collaborated enthusiastically from the start in the seemingly endless hours of debate and consultation. His special knowledge of the history of public health, exemplified in his teaching and in the splendid opening chapter of the new [1984] *Oxford Textbook of Public Health*, was particularly welcome . . . All this was not enough and he undertook much of the administration of the Social Medicine Unit's study of exercise in leisure-time and the incidence of coronary heart disease among civil servants. This involved three large national surveys between 1968 and 1984; his patience, good humour, capacity for detail and superlative human relations again assured a first-class job. Countless colleagues and old students – his friends – across the world remember with affection this gentle and scholarly man and extend their sympathy to his devoted widow and family'.

In recognition of Sidney's distinguished career at the School, he was presented with a specially engraved silver medal to mark his completion of 50 years of service to the School, and on his retirement in 1979, by resolution of the board of management of the School, the title of Emeritus Senior Lecturer in Public Health was conferred upon him – a most unusual distinction. After his death, a room in the Department of Community Health was re-equipped and refurnished through contributions from his many friends and was named 'The Sidney Chave Room'.

It was not only in the School that Sidney Chave achieved distinction. He always put a lot of himself into any activity he took up, whether this was ornithology, numismatology, heraldry, the Society for the Social History of Medicine or his contributions to his local church and parish council. The first informal meeting of the founders of the Society for the

Social History of Medicine (of which Sidney was one) met in his room at the School in early 1969. Sidney was a member of the first executive committee of the Society, and gave one of the first historical papers in 1970. In 1971 Sidney was the vice-chairman and treasurer, and on the retirement of Huw Francis became chairman later that year. In 1975 he was president of the Society, and was again vice-chairman in 1976 and chairman in 1979. These offices reflect the esteem of his colleagues and give some, although inadequate, indication of the many contributions he made to the establishment, growth and reputation of the Society.

Other honours that were bestowed upon Sidney include the election to honorary membership of the Society of Social Medicine, his appointment as the Monckton Copeman Lecturer of the Worshipful Society of Apothecaries in 1979 and the invitation from the University of Liverpool to give the Inaugural Duncan Memorial Lecture in 1983. (Both of these addresses are reproduced in this book.) In 1977 he was awarded the Queen's Jubilee Medal.

Some achieve as much as Sidney did only by some disregard of their family and neighbours. This was not Sidney's way; somehow along with his busy professional life, he managed to be a devoted son, husband, father and grandfather and to give much to his church and parish. At various times he was a member, and secretary, of his local parochial church council, chairman of the Youth Fellowship Committee, parish representative to the Canterbury Diocesan Conference, churchwarden, and, in later years, a Guildsman of St Bride's, Fleet Street. It is, therefore, fitting to finish this tribute with the words of the Rev Frank Doe, one-time vicar of St Oswald's:

'Sidney Chave was closely associated with St Oswald's Church, Norbury, from the time he and Eileen were married there until his death. During those years he held with flair and distinction a succession of offices. By the congregation, and by a succession of vicars, he was held in affection, respect and admiration. In committee he was a welcome asset, for his command of the English language was such that he could at short notice, or indeed at no notice at all, sum up a situation or an argument succinctly and peacefully. If Sidney was a born teacher, as I believe he was, he was also a born peacemaker'.

Michael Warren
1987

WRITINGS
BY
SIDNEY CHAVE

1

The first medical officer of health

*Duncan of Liverpool – and some lessons for today**

I want to begin this lecture not with Duncan, but with the man who more than anyone else was responsible for starting it all; the man those of us who work in the broad fields of public and community health still look on as our godfather – I refer, of course, to Edwin Chadwick [1800–1890]. Chadwick's long life spanned 90 years of the last century. He lived through the battles of Waterloo and Peterloo; the Corn Laws and the Crimean War; he saw the Great Exhibition and the coming of the Great Western Railway. All these events, and what they represented, must form the unspoken but assumed background against which we should see the life and work of William Henry Duncan.

But to continue with Chadwick, in his well-known *Report on the Sanitary Condition of the Labouring Population* he wrote the following paragraph:

> 'That for the general means necessary to prevent disease, it would be good economy to appoint a district medical officer, independent of private practice, with the securities of special qualifications, and responsibilities to initiate sanitary measures and reclaim the execution of the law'.

This was the moment of conception of the medical officer of health – the MOH. And that was in 1842. Five years later, after a somewhat troubled gestation, he came to birth in Liverpool in the person of William Henry Duncan. But why Liverpool? and why Duncan? Why indeed!

---

* The Inaugural Duncan Memorial Lecture delivered at the University of Liverpool on 23 November 1983, and reprinted from *Community Medicine* (1984) 6:61–71.

Liverpool is well-known as a famous port with a long history. It thrived on the slave trade, being one of the ports of call on the triangular route on which that revolting commerce was based. Then later as industrial development took place in Lancashire in the 19th century, Liverpool became the principal port both for the import of raw materials and for the export of manufactured goods across the world. But Liverpool manufactured very little for itself; rather it was a staging post in this two-way traffic.

So what characterised the working population in the town at that time, and what distinguished it from the main Lancashire towns, was that it was composed not of workers employed in factories and mills getting regular wages, small as they might be, but that it consisted very largely of unskilled casual labourers without regular employment. It was casual labourers who came to Liverpool to build the docks, and it was casual labourers, the dockers, who loaded and unloaded the ships. Theirs was a particularly vulnerable occupation, for when the ships came in there was work for them to do, but when there were no ships, they stood idle, and any down-turn in trade brought unemployment and destitution. All this meant that they had very little money with which to obtain the essentials of life in terms of food, clothing and shelter. In particular, they could afford only the meanest housing accommodation and that is exactly what they got.

Houses were hastily built without regard to suitability of soil or site, for water supply or sanitation. Hundreds of dwellings were packed together in narrow courts with an opening at one end only. And the people were packed together inside them, literally from cellar to attic. Accumulations of refuse and soil-heaps, and evil-smelling and overflowing cesspools were common features of this unwholesome environment.

Dirt, disease and malnourishment flourished. Chief among the diseases were typhoid and typhus, which had not by then been distinguished and were known together as 'the fever'. There was dysentery, scarlet fever, measles and, of course, tuberculosis – 'the captain of the men of death'. Then there was cholera which was the Victorian equivalent of the mediaeval Black Death and which, since the successful introduction of vaccination, had replaced smallpox as the epidemic disease most to be feared.

Such then was Liverpool in the year 1840. The picture can be summed up not in a word, but in a figure; that figure was 36. The annual death rate in Liverpool was 36 per 1,000 and that was the highest in the country. Liverpool was, in fact, the most unhealthy town in the kingdom, hence Liverpool. But why Duncan?

Historians are in some ways like epidemiologists. As epidemiologists, when investigating the occurrence of disease, we are trained to look for three factors, time, place and person, as pointers to the origin of the outbreak. So does the historian; when seeking to understand the occurrence of some historical event, he looks for the relevant circumstances at the time and in the place where the event occurred, but then there is generally the person who in some way, perhaps through speech, thought or action, or perhaps all three, was instrumental in bringing the event to pass.

So it was in Liverpool at the time, and in the circumstances that we have been considering. Which brings us to William Henry Duncan.

Frazer [1947] tells us that Duncan was a Liverpolitan born and bred. He was born in Seel Street, then one of the more salubrious areas of the town, in 1805, the year of the Battle of Trafalgar – an event itself significant to Liverpool for it reopened the sea-lanes to maritime trade once again. Young William was the third son and the fifth child of his father, a merchant whose business was in the town. His mother, who came from a clerical family, was a Scot from Dumfries.

We believe he attended school in the town after which he went up to Edinburgh to study medicine. He graduated MD at the age of 25 with a thesis written in impeccable Latin entitled *De ventris in reliquum corpus potestate*. While in Edinburgh he would certainly have heard about the work and writings of Johann Peter Frank [1745–1821] and his system of 'medicinischen polizey', or medical police [nine volumes published 1779–1827]. In this massive work Frank argued with great cogency, and showed in great detail, how the state could, and indeed should, assume responsibility for the health and welfare of all its citizens, and should ensure this by regulating their every behaviour from the cradle to the grave. Frank's work was held in high esteem by the Scottish academics.

But the idea of medical police was not to the taste of the English with their Victorian values where laissez-faire, sturdy independence, and unfettered private enterprise was the accepted dogma.

Only gradually under the unanswerable case for state intervention to control private interests in favour of the public weal, which was advanced first, and unsuccessfully, by Chadwick, and somewhat later, but more diplomatically by Simon [1816–1904], did this characteristically English philosophy begin to break down. But all that lay in the future.

The seed of this idea had been sown in Duncan's mind and he returned to his native soil to tend its development.

On his return to Liverpool, he immediately began to take an active part in the professional and social life of the town. He took up residence at 54 Rodney Street, which became the family home, and commenced to practise. He joined the Liverpool Medical Institution (the subscription list shows that he subscribed the sum of five pounds towards the erection of the present building in Hope Street). In 1837 he became president of the Liverpool Medical Society. Shortly after he was appointed lecturer in medical jurisprudence in the medical school at the Royal Institution. In addition to all this he became a member of the Athenaeum and was also a regular attender at the meetings of the Liverpool Literary and Philosophical Society; and this was to prove to be important later on.

But let us now turn to his professional life. As I said, he took up private practice at first among the Liverpolitans of his own class. In this he soon became a successful young practitioner with a circle of patients among the well-to-do – and there was nothing remarkable about that. But then, for his own reasons, he took a post as an honorary physician to the dispensaries which catered for the sick poor, working first at the North Dispensary and then later at the South Dispensary which was located at 1 Upper Parliament Street. These dispensaries were supported in part by the parish and in part by charity.

It was here that Duncan first came face to face with the twin-related evils that had already confronted Chadwick, namely dire sickness and abject poverty. There is no doubt that Duncan was moved by what he saw at first hand in those overcrowded hovels and insanitary courts. This was the first step along the path which was to take him into public health.

When in 1832 cholera struck Liverpool for the first time, he was working among both sections of the community – the upper class Liverpolitans and the working class Liverpudlians. He was immediately struck by how much greater were the casualties of the epidemic among the poor and overcrowded, than they were among the better off and better housed. So he wrote a paper on this for the *Liverpool Medical Gazette*, the first of a number of such papers that he contributed to his local journal. In these papers he invariably referred to the insanitary conditions prevailing in the poorer parts of the town.

When in 1840, the House of Commons Select Committee on the Health of Towns visited Liverpool, Duncan appeared before them as a witness and gave evidence on what he called 'the bad pre-eminence of the worst population density in the land'. He reported that one third of the working class lived in Liverpool's typical narrow and airless courts and one eighth lived in underground cellars. The public lodging houses, of which there were hundreds, were packed to the doors often with thirty people sleeping in a cellar. Only four of the twenty miles of streets in the working class areas were sewered. No wonder, he said, the fevers were 'rampant'.

The Committee were obviously impressed. They recorded his evidence in their proceedings, but no action followed. Later in the same year he submitted a written report in the same terms in answer to an enquiry by the Poor Law Commission, which had been initiated by Chadwick. Here he cited the example of one court of twelve houses where, because of the complete absence of any kind of drainage, the whole court was permanently inundated with filth, and in those twelve houses, he said, there had been no fewer than 63 cases of fever.

This was probably Duncan's first contact with Chadwick who was then secretary, and chief executive officer, to the Poor Law Commission. There were to be many more such contacts in the years to follow.

It is worth making the point here that Duncan shared the work at the dispensaries with several other colleagues, all of whom must have seen the same destitution, degradation and distress in the districts which were served by the dispensaries, but only one of them did anything about it, and that was William Henry Duncan.

By now Duncan had twice reported to official enquiries about the mean and stinking conditions in which so many of his fellow townsfolk were compelled to live, and die. It seems that he was not satisfied simply to continue to be a witness to others, he now began to be active in this cause in his own right.

He had by this time marshalled a body of evidence concerning the unhealthiness of Liverpool; he now re-organised and expanded this material and used it to prepare two lectures under the title of 'The physical causes of the high rate of mortality in Liverpool'. And he delivered these two lectures not, as you might expect, to the Medical Society, not to the doctors, but to the Literary and Philosophical Society, of which, as I mentioned earlier, he was a member.

Why did he choose this audience of lay people in preference to his medical colleagues? Almost certainly, to bring what he had to say to a wider audience, and to an audience which included some of the best educated and most influential people in the town. Good tactics this – and one which we might do well to follow when we have a case to make.

The lectures achieved what he had hoped; they were widely reported round the town and aroused considerable local interest. Duncan then followed this up by publishing the text of the lectures in pamphlet form, under the same title.

The pamphlet, better described as a booklet, consisted of 76 printed pages. In it he set out fully the mortality in Liverpool and made some comparisons with other areas. Some of these comparisons might well make our modern statisticians' hair stand on end, because he was not always comparing like with like and knew nothing about standardisation. But then, he had not the benefits, and delights, of Bradford Hill's little book *Principles of Medical Statistics* [first edition 1937] to put him on the right lines! So, delving into William Farr's handiwork at the General Register Office he showed that the average age of death in the County of Wiltshire was 36.5 years whereas in Liverpool it was only 19 years. He then went on to explain this high mortality in terms of the prevailing theory of the miasma. This held that the fevers were caused by foul air rising from the decomposition, the putrefaction, of organic matter and waste. This view was held by the great majority of his colleagues in the medical profession; it was the view held by the sanitary reformers; it was the view held by Chadwick himself. Indeed, Chadwick's own work was taken to give proof to the theory, for it was in the most overcrowded, unsewered and unventilated quarters that the incidence of the fevers invariably reached its peak. This was the basic premise on which Chadwick had built his 'Sanitary Idea' which was to infuse the public health movement for the next fifty years, and which led to his simple and sovereign remedy for the prevention of fevers, namely a drainage system backed by a supply of running water to flush away the filth and disease-causing odours deriving from it.

Duncan, in pursuing his own inquiries in Liverpool, reached the same general conclusion as to the cause, but he gave greater weight to what he called 'vitiated air' derived from respiring human beings. This, he claimed, became particularly dangerous when associated with the effluvia arising from putrefaction, and more especially so when confined in enclosed spaces. However, as for Chadwick, so for Duncan, the remedy was the same – reduction in overcrowding, improved ventilation and an effective system of drainage.

The publication of the pamphlet aroused much discussion

in the town, as well as some mixed feelings. There were those, whom we might call the local patriots, who accused him of denigrating 'the good old town' as they called it. A local surgeon was bold enough to try to refute Duncan's statistics – but he had not read Bradford Hill either! Duncan went back to the Registrar General's reports yet again and from these he showed that the annual death rate in Liverpool was 1 in 28 persons, whereas in Birmingham it was 1 in 36 and in London it was 1 in 37.

By all the yardsticks Liverpool really was the most unhealthy town in the country and, by now, largely due to Duncan, the town knew it. Things began to move.

In 1845, as a result of growing feeling, the mayor called a public meeting which was addressed at some length by Duncan, the object of which was to form a Health of Towns Association, similar to the one which had been set up in London in the previous year. Its object was:

> 'to bring the subject of sanitary reform under the notice of every class of the community, to diffuse sound principles as widely as possible by meetings, lectures, and publications, and especially to give information on all points connected with the sanitary conditions of Liverpool, and the means of improving it.'

The association was formed and soon won the support of many of the prominent people in the town.

This led directly to the next step which came in the following year when the council promoted a private bill in Parliament seeking wide powers to pursue a programme of sanitary reform and, most significantly, the bill included a clause empowering the council to appoint a medical officer of health.

The bill passed through Parliament without demur as the Liverpool Sanatory Act 1846. It was a milestone in the history of English public health, for it was the first comprehensive sanitary act to be passed into law, and it gave authority for the appointment of an MOH.

It is worth the comment, that when a year later the City of London copied the example of Liverpool and obtained similar powers also to appoint an MOH, it advertised the post, received 20 applications and appointed the youngest of them, namely John Simon.

But in the case of Liverpool there was only one possible candidate. The council went through the motions of setting up a special committee to consider the appointment of an MOH. The committee immediately offered Duncan the post and he immediately accepted. On 1 January 1847 the Secretary of State confirmed the appointment, as the act required, and on that day William Henry Duncan became the first medical officer of health in British history. Liverpool deserves the credit for having made this appointment but then Liverpool, above all other towns in the country, needed him the most.

Duncan was aged 42; on his appointment his salary was £300 a year with the right to continue with his private practice. However, he soon found this arrangement incompatible with his official duties. For one thing, he could have found himself in an invidious position if he had had to take action against a landlord who was one of his patients. Moreover, this arrangement did not accord with Chadwick's wishes who had always argued against part-time appointments. So, after a year, the appointment was made full-time at a salary of £750. This despite the opposition of one councillor who thought that the money would be better spent on limewashing the town, and another who argued strongly that you did not need a doctor to do this job anyway. And how many times since then have we heard that argument!

It is not easy for us to enter into Duncan's feelings on that morning when he went into his office for the first time, because he never told us. He was a somewhat reserved man who wrote little outside his official correspondence and his formal reports. Certainly we know that at the start he had no assistance or support of any kind. It is true that there was Mr Fresh, the Inspector of Nuisances, who was also appointed under the act, but although he was to work closely with Duncan, he was an independent officer of the council.

Duncan had no precedents to guide him, no colleagues anywhere in the country with whom he might discuss his problems, his programme or his plans.

Yet he was not altogether without some guidelines and these were provided, surprisingly enough, by the clause in the act under which he was appointed. And although the clause is a long one, I want to quote part of it because it was to be an important statement in its own right. It reads:

'It shall be lawful for the said Council to appoint, subject to the approval of one of Her Majesty's Secretaries of State, a legally qualified medical practitioner of skill and experience to inspect and report periodically on the sanitary state of the said borough, to ascertain the existence of diseases, more especially of epidemics increasing the rate of mortality, and to point out the existence of any nuisances or other local causes which are likely to originate and maintain such diseases, and injuriously affect inhabitants of the said borough, and to take cognisance of the fact of the existence of any contagious disease, and so to point out the most efficacious means for checking and preventing the spread of such diseases, and also to point out the most efficient means for the ventilation of churches, chapels, schools, registered lodging houses and other public edifices within the said borough ... and such person shall be called the Medical Officer of Health for the Borough of Liverpool, and it shall be lawful for the said Council to pay such Officer such salary as shall be approved by one of Her Majesty's Principal Secretaries of State.'

This then was the original job specification of the MOH and, incidentally, it is the first mention of the title of medical officer of health in any act of Parliament, or indeed, in any official document.

So, he had to 'inspect and report' on all matters which might injuriously affect the public health, to advise on such actions which should be taken to deal with them, and to have special regard to infectious diseases. The emphasis laid on the need for proper ventilation of public buildings shows the general acceptance of the theory of the miasma. This clause was to be quoted many times in the years to come.

So perhaps, in our imagination, we can picture Duncan

like Saint George as he sallied forth armed with the weapons forged by Chadwick to combat the Monster Miasma. Well a monster it proved to be, or rather a hydra, because the monster was soon shown to be many-headed. For Duncan's luck was out, because the next three years turned out to be the most calamitous in Liverpool's history. It all began with the Irish potato famine. This had started in 1845 with the failure of the potato crop and in the next two years it reached disastrous proportions. Starvation was widespread. Driven by hunger, thousands of Irish peasants migrated to England, and they travelled by way of Liverpool. At times they were being landed at the rate of 900 a day, the fare for standing room on the deck being only sixpence a head.

Duncan reported later to the council 'that not less than 300,000 Irish have landed in Liverpool. Of these it is estimated that from 60,000 to 80,000 have located themselves amongst us, occupying every nook and cranny of the already overcrowded lodging-houses and forcing their way into cellars of which there are several thousand still remaining in the town.'

The inevitable result of this influx of desperately poor, unwashed and starving people was a massive outbreak of typhus. Within a short time hospitals were packed to the doors with patients lying three to a bed. Emergency accommodation was opened wherever possible. Duncan obtained permission to make use of ships anchored in the docks. And still the cases admitted were exceeded twice over by those for whom no accommodation could be provided. Beyond this there was little that Duncan could do save practise his sanitary principles – remove such cases as he could and cleanse and limewash infected premises and districts.

At the end of the year he estimated that nearly 60,000 people had suffered from fever while a further 40,000 had contracted either diarrhoea or dysentery. There were, he said, 8,500 deaths from these causes: smallpox had also occurred and carried off 380 children, while measles had added a similar number to the total. Altogether the toll of deaths from all causes that year amounted to no less than one in 14 of the population of the town. It was the most fatal year in the annals of Liverpool, and it was the first year that Liverpool had had a medical officer of health.

The epidemic subsided in the following year although the death rate from infectious diseases still remained high – a severe outbreak of scarlet fever carried off over 1,500 victims, while tuberculosis accounted for 1,400 more, although there was nothing exceptional about that.

But Duncan's troubles were not over, because in 1849 a family of emigrants arrived by steamer from Dumfries where cholera was raging. Three of these newcomers developed cholera and died within a few days. Then a woman in the same house went down with the disease, and then another, and another and within a short time the outbreak was spreading in all directions. It cut through the crowded populations in those courts and tenements like the sickle of death. Duncan again instituted his sanitary programme, and, in addition, he introduced a system of medical visitors who went round the affected areas seeking out cases in their early stages and starting such treatment as was then available. But at times the outbreak reached overwhelming proportions. At its peak there were over 500 deaths in a week and mass burials in open pits were resorted to, as in the days of the plague. Altogether there were over 5,000 deaths from cholera that year.

After those three crisis years in which the new medical officer of health must have felt himself to have been well and truly 'blooded', there was a return to some kind of 'normality', if one can use that term for such a town as Liverpool then was.

Shortly after the ending of the first epidemic Duncan had written 'fever prevails at all times to a greater or lesser extent among the poor of Liverpool and must continue to prevail so long as their habitations are constructed so as to accumulate filth and to exclude the air of heaven.'

The appalling housing conditions prevailing in the poorer parts of the town were his biggest problem. And the worst features of these were the cellar-dwellings for which Liverpool had become notorious. In fact, the use of cellars as habitations had been banned by law in 1842. Nevertheless in

1847 Duncan found there were still about 30,000 people living in 8,000 of these underground, unlit, unventilated quarters.

While still coping with the epidemic, indeed, as part of his plan of action, Duncan launched a massive programme of clearance of the cellars. At the outset these evictions caused great hardship to these unfortunate people, large numbers of whom were left standing in the street. So within a short time, Duncan re-phased the programme so that not more than 100 cellars were cleared in a month, thus giving some opportunity for the people to find somewhere else to go.

Duncan reported on the reluctance of the inmates to leave their miserable abodes because of the facilities offered by the entrances to the cellars 'for the sale of cakes, fruit, vegetables and chips!'. Duncan continued 'and so strong is the feeling that were it not for constant and systematic inspection, the cellars would be re-occupied as soon as they were cleared'.

After three years of determined effort Duncan succeeded in reducing the proportion of people in these downtown areas who were living in cellars from 12 per cent to 2 per cent. No small achievement this, but won at no little social cost.

The relationships between Duncan and his authorities were not always easy and, at times, he must have been glad of the measure of independence attaching to his post. The select vestry proved to be particularly difficult. This body corresponded to the boards of guardians elsewhere. It was the select vestry, and not the borough council, which was responsible for the provision of hospital accommodation for the poor, as well as for the relief of destitution. The vestry continually resented being called upon to spend money to expand hospital provision by Duncan, who, as MOH, was not directly responsible to them.

The dispute came to a head in 1854 when cholera came again. At first the vestry flatly refused to admit that there was cholera in the town at all. Then, when the epidemic exploded, they took legal advice and declared that it was outside the province of the medical officer of health to recommend 'curative measures', it was his duty simply to 'inspect and report'. Duncan replied by quoting the clause in the act which required him to 'point out the most efficacious means for checking and preventing the spread of epidemic disease'. The issue was serious enough to be referred to the General Board of Health in London for a ruling. The board, advised by Chadwick, found in favour of Duncan. It was a victory for him, but more than that, it established a very important principle for the future, which was to last down to our own day.

Duncan's relations with the borough council and its sanitary committee were almost invariably good. In general, they were very supportive of all that he tried to do. But we must remember that they had never had an MOH before, so they had some learning to do as well.

It is apparent that in Duncan's early years the council were by no means open-handed in providing him with assistance nor even in covering his necessary expenses.

When in 1851 the town clerk asked the various departmental heads to submit a nominal roll of their staff, Duncan replied, perhaps with a touch of wry humour: 'The following list comprises the whole of the officer in my department paid by the Corporation, William Henry Duncan MD, Medical Officer of Health.'

After four years he was still working alone.

In a letter to the town clerk written in the same year, he complained that he had paid out of his own pocket upwards of £20 for assistance in his office and had employed his own servant as a messenger. He went on to point out that he had also used his own gig with his horse and groom at an estimated cost to himself of £90.

These were among the teething problems of the new office. In time the council provided him with clerical staff, and five lodging-house inspectors. Later still, a Dr Cameron was appointed to act as his deputy.

But they never raised his salary! This had been fixed at £750 in 1848 and there it remained for the next 15 years. Although, let it be said in Liverpool's favour, that this was more than any other MOH in the land was being paid at that time.

The years following the great epidemics saw steady

improvements in the living and working conditions in Liverpool, especially in the poorer districts. The worst of the sanitary evils were swept away. Private building was controlled; landlords were no longer allowed to build houses in narrow courts and without proper sanitary facilities. Drainage, water supplies, street cleansing and waste disposal were all improved. These improvements were reflected in measureable improvements in the health of the inhabitants. The mortality rate fell from 36 per 1,000 in 1846 to 28 per 1,000 in 1860, while the average age at death rose from 19 years in 1846 to 25.5 years in 1860. Such changes in mortality statistics may seem small to us today but they represented the saving of many hundreds of lives in a town with a population of 400,000.

After 1860 Duncan's health began to fail and he died three years later at the age of 57 while still in office.

Throughout the 16 years during which he had held the post of medical officer of health, Duncan had carried out his duties conscientiously and well. In tackling the immense problems which faced him he took sensible, practical action based on his belief in the miasma. If the theory was wrong, the action was right. The citizens of Liverpool had good reason to be grateful for his dedication to the sanitary task which undoubtedly brought them substantial benefits.

But more than this William Henry Duncan was a trail-blazer who, working very largely single-handed and with very limited resources, pointed the way along the path of sanitary reform and health improvement which his successors in office were to follow through the remainder of the century and even after.

How can we sum up Duncan, assess his contribution and his place in history? He made no original discoveries; he did not contribute to national policy. In this respect he was overshadowed by his more famous contemporary, John Simon. For whereas Simon moved from the local to the national stage, and played his part there, and did so supremely well, Duncan remained in the local scene, playing his part in that more restricted setting, but doing so there with equal success.

Without in any way intending to be derogatory one can say that he was the local lad who made good. But he made much good; for Liverpool was a much better place for its people to live in as a result of his 16 years of unremitting toil.

But what was his legacy? As we have seen he has one distinction which cannot be taken away: he was the first man in. His was the first footprint in the sand and in this he left an enduring mark.

When five years after his death Alexander Stewart [1867] carried out a sanitary survey in the towns of England, he found that many large towns including Manchester, Birmingham and Sheffield had not even bothered to appoint an MOH; they regarded him as an expensive luxury they could afford to do without. But when he came to Liverpool how different is his report. 'There,' he writes, '*the Officer of Health is not only a reality; he is a power in the commonwealth*. He is recognized by the civic authorities as their official adviser whose opinion is asked for and listened to with deference in all matters relating to the public health, and having proved himself worthy of their confidence, he has been entrusted with very large discretionary powers which he has exercised with great tact and judgement in furtherance of the views of the health committees and the Sanitary Acts.' An eloquent testimony to the groundwork laid by Duncan and his immediate successor William Trench.

But what has all this got to do with us and our concerns today? Has history any light to shed on our present? Let me offer a few tentative thoughts.

Duncan shared with us the belief that prevention is to be preferred to cure, where it makes sense to speak of cure. But where it does not, as with so many of the chronic conditions of today, I think he would have agreed that prevention is better than treatment, especially when that treatment takes us into high and costly medical technology, or involves continuing care perhaps lasting a lifetime. The case for prevention remains as strong in our day as in his.

Duncan was well aware of what we now call 'the inequalities in health', indeed, he faced them, and this is a problem that continues to plague us today, as the writings of Professor

Morris [1979] and others have shown. And indeed, Merseyside still looms large in the ranks of the deprived areas of the country.

Housing, bad housing, with all its evil ramifications, still remains a problem here as elsewhere; and Toxteth, which for Duncan meant a pleasant suburb with a park and a hospital, has come to have other connotations associated not so much with disease as with disorder. But, is the new public health concerned with these problems; or have we cut ourselves off from our roots? I think perhaps we have.

William Henry Duncan was a medical sanitarian working in the field of traditional public health. He was faced with the problems of cholera and the other fevers. Today's community physician, working in and developing the new public health, is concerned not with cholera but with coronaries, with cancer, with chronic conditions and addictions. Duncan's problems stemmed largely from dirt, deficiency and deprivation, ours largely from excess – from excessive smoking, eating, drinking, speeding, licence. Duncan's targets were filth and overcrowding: ours are behaviour and lifestyle.

Duncan tackled his problems through the methods of what we now call primary prevention, that is, the methods of environmental control. We tackle ours through health education and the screening programmes and therapies of secondary and tertiary prevention.

Would that our methods were as certain as his! But let us not be disheartened. Remember, it took fifty years from Duncan's appointment before the public health movement could look up from its work and say 'Well, that's that, we have now cleaned up the worst evils of an insanitary environment, cholera and the fevers have been overcome.' Then, with the turn of the century they took up the task of creating and developing the personal health services we have with us today.

We still have some time left before the end of our present century, time in which, if we are persistent and painstaking in applying the best we know, as Duncan did, we may yet achieve a breakthrough towards a reduction in the incidence of the plagues that have affected our society since the war. By which I mean coronary heart disease, lung cancer, death and disablement on the road, the large but largely hidden problem of alcoholism, the rising problem of drug addiction, and the massive problem of unwanted pregnancies.

Time still to break the back of these problems if we buckle to the task. But time too, I think, to remind ourselves that it is sixty years since Lord Dawson [1864–1945] introduced us to the idea of the health centre with his famous dictum that 'Preventive and curative medicine cannot be separated on any known principle'. Time at long last to take that lesson really to heart and through the setting up of good primary health care centres and services out in the community to bring that dictum to reality. Recently, Tudor Hart [1981] and others have proposed that the doctors in these centres should take on the responsibility for the public health in their neighbourhoods. This might require a new kind of doctor – a practitioner of curative and preventive medicine and of the wider public health. If it does mean that, so be it. We created a new kind of doctor here in Liverpool in 1847, we did it again in 1974, we could do it again by 1994, perhaps even here in Liverpool. A practitioner of medicine and health? That's a thought! But let me leave that thought there and return again to Duncan.

When an outbreak of infectious disease occurred in Liverpool, the first that Duncan knew about it was when he was notified of a death, by which time the epidemic could have been well under way and it would have been too late to do much about it.

It did not take the medical officers of health long to realise that what they needed was the immediate notification of the first case. So through their collective voice, the Society of Medical Officers of Health, they began to agitate for the compulsory notification of infectious diseases. The general practitioners did not want this. They regarded it as an unwarranted intrusion in their private practice. The government did not want it either because they feared that it might lead to an increased demand for hospital accommodation. But, undaunted, the MOsH continued their pressure until, in the end, they won the day and got what they asked for. That was the old, the traditional, public health.

Now where is the collective voice of the new public health? Who speaks to government today about the anti-health factors in our society, about the opposition to fluoridation, or sports sponsorship by tobacco interests or 'inequalities' or the needs of inner cities or of the mentally handicapped or the elderly? Have we handed over our responsibilities to ASH, to the Child Poverty Action Group, to SHELTER, to MIND and to Age Concern? And if so, for what benefit? Was it just to achieve a tidy system of administration for the health service?

Duncan and his successors developed and practised what became the characteristic, the traditional, roles of the MOH. He was at once public watchdog and accuser, he was adviser and initiator, he was educator and protector.

Now who exercises these roles today? The environmental health officer perhaps. Dr Duncan never passed his responsibilities over to Mr Fresh. But perhaps we do not need them any more. Are our roles as manager, monitor and manipulator of resources enough? I wonder.

Forty years ago, William Beveridge [1879–1963] spoke of the five giants which would assail our society after the war. They were Ignorance, Idleness, Squalor, Want and Disease. These giants did not first see the light of day in 1945. Duncan knew them well enough here in Liverpool in 1845 and we do not have to look far to find them here still. They remain a continuing challenge to all those who are concerned with the well-being of the people of this city and this country, and not least, to those who are practitioners of *community health* in its widest sense. Can we lift our eyes from our desks to meet it? I think we can – I think we should.

Finally, next year, the community physician will reach the age of ten. He will no longer be a toddler, he will have found his feet. In six years time, in 1990, he will have served the community at large for as long as Duncan did his, here in Liverpool.

Would that some scribe will write of him then, as he once wrote of Duncan: *He is not only a reality; he is a power in the commonwealth.*

Writings by Sidney Chave

ACKNOWLEDGEMENTS

I would like to record my thanks to Professor R Shields, Dean of the Faculty of Medicine, and Dr JR Ashton of the Department of Community Health in the University of Liverpool, who were responsible for arranging the lecture; to my colleagues in the Department of Community Health at the London School of Hygiene and Tropical Medicine for their helpful comments; to Miss J Smith, Liverpool City Archivist for her assistance; and to Miss Beth Shaw for clerical help.

The Health Education Council generously provided support for the lecture.

BIBLIOGRAPHY

Bradford Hill A. Principles of medical statistics (1st edition). London, Lancet, 1937.

Brockington CF. Public health in the nineteenth century. London, Livingstone, 1965.

Chave SPW. The rise and fall of the medical officer of health. Community Health, 1980, 2, 36. (*See chapter 6*)

Duncan WH. The physical causes of the high rate of mortality in Liverpool. Liverpool, 1844.

Duncan WH. The letter books 1849–1863. (Three volumes, unpublished MSS, Liverpool City Archives).

Duncan WH. Report to the health committee on the health of the town. Liverpool, Harris, during the years 1847–48–49–50, then annually 1851 to 1860.

Finer SE. The life and times of Sir Edwin Chadwick. London, Methuen, 1952.

Flinn MW (ed). Report on the sanitary condition of the labouring population of Great Britain (Chadwick E, 1842). Edinburgh, University Press, 1964.

Frazer WH. Duncan of Liverpool. London, Hamish Hamilton, 1947.

Frazer WM. A history of English public health, 1839–1939. London, Baillière, Tindall and Cox, 1950.

Hope EW. Health at the gateway. Cambridge, University Press, 1931.

Hyde FE. Liverpool and the Mersey. Newton Abbot, David and Charles, 1971.

Interdepartmental committee on social insurance and allied services report (Beveridge report). London, HMSO, 1942.

Lambert R. Sir John Simon, 1816–1904 and English social administration. London, MacGibban and Kee, 1963.

Lewis RA. Edwin Chadwick and the public health movement, 1832–1854. London, Longmans, 1952.

Liverpool Sanatory Act, 1846. Vic. 9 and 10, Cap 127, CXXII.

Midwinter EC. Old Liverpool. Newton Abbot, David and Charles, 1971.

Ministry of Health. Consultative Council on Medical and Allied Services. Interim report on the future provision of medical and allied services (Dawson report). London, HMSO, 1920.

Morris JN. Tomorrow's community physician. The Lancet, 1969, 2, p 811.

Morris JN. Social inequalities undiminished. The Lancet, 1979, 1, p 87.

Muir JRB. A history of Liverpool. London, Williams and Norgate, 1907.

Poor Law Commission. Reports on the sanitary condition of local populations of England, No 19, Liverpool. London, HMSO, 1842.

Public Health, Jubilee Number, 1905, chapters 3–5.

Punch. The value of health in Liverpool. 1847, 12, p 44.

Royal commission for inquiring into the state of large towns and populous districts. (Chairman, Duke of Buccleuch) First report: section on 'Special reports on the sanitary condition of several towns'. (No 1, Liverpool.) London, HMSO, 1844.

Simon J. English sanitary institutions. London, Cassell, 1890.

Stewart A. The medical and legal aspects of sanitary reform. London, Hardwicke, 1867.

Townsend P (ed). Inequalities in health (Black report). Harmondsworth, Penguin, 1982.

Tudor Hart J. A new kind of doctor. Journal of the Royal Society of Medicine, 1981, 74, p 871.

2

Men who did honour to their profession

When in 1847 the vicar of Christ Church, Regents Park, enquired into the procedure for having the streets of his parish cleansed he was informed that 'in the parish of St Pancras where you reside, there are 16 separate pavings boards acting under 29 Acts of Parliament all of which would have to be consulted on this matter'. There were, in addition, five lighting boards serving his parish; and on these 21 boards there sat 900 commissioners. This was typical of the 'system' of local administration which prevailed in London at that time, for London was a geographical rather than an administrative entity. Because of the complexity of the situation and also because of the powerful vested interests involved, London had been excluded from the provisions of the Municipal Corporations Act of 1835 so that it continued to remain an insanitary and legal chaos. There were in the capital over 300 local bodies dabbling in its administration, including seven commissions of sewerage (with 1,065 members), 172 vestries and boards of guardians, and more than 100 paving, lighting and cleansing boards, many of whose members were self-elected for life. The main activities of these bodies were concerned with wrangling over their respective jurisdiction and their perquisites. In consequence, the inhabitants of London suffered, but as elsewhere, it was the poorest who suffered most.

Their plight is perhaps best brought out by a letter sent by some of the inhabitants of Soho and published in *The Times* on 5 July 1849. It read as follows:

A SANITARY REMONSTRANCE

We print the following remonstrance just as it has reached us, and trust its publication will assist the unfortunate remonstrants:—

THE EDITUR OF THE TIMES PAPER

Sur, – May we beg and beseach your proteckshion and power, We are Sur, as it may be, livin in a Willderniss, so far as the rest of London knows anything of us, or as the rich and great people care about. We live in muck and filthe. We aint got no priviz, no dust bins, no drains, no water-splies, and no drain or suer in the hole place. The Suer Company, in Greek St., Soho Square, all great, rich and powerfool men, take no notice watsomedever of our cumplaints. The Stenche of a Gully-hole is disgustin. We all of us suffur, and numbers are ill, and if the Colera comes Lord help us.

Some gentlemans comed yesterday, and we thought they was comishioners from the Suer Company, but they was complaining of the noosance and stenche our lanes and corts was to them in New Oxforde Street. They was much surprized to see the seller in No. 12, Carrier St., on our lane, where a child was dyin from fever, and would not beleave that Sixty persons sleep in it every night. This here seller you couldent swing a cat in, and the rent is five shilling a week; but theare are greate many sich deare sellers. Sur, we hope you will let us have our cumplaints put into your hinfluenshall paper, and make these land-lords of our houses and these comishioners (the friends we spose of the landlords) make our houses decent for Christions to live in.

Preaye Sir com and see us, for we are livin like piggs, and it aint faire we should be so ill treted.

We are your respeckfull servents in Church Lane, Carrier St., and the other corts.
Teusday, Juley 3, 1849

There were 54 signatures appended to this letter, the facts and authenticity of which were confirmed by the paper. The letter speaks for itself. The conditions it describes could have been multiplied many times across London and, not least, in the back streets of the City, as Simon had already found.

It was in 1855 that, at long last, the government grasped the nettle and introduced a bill effecting the reforms which had been resisted for so long. Entitled 'An act for the better local management of the metropolis', it embodied two important principles which, in the end, were to be applied to the country as a whole. London was divided into 46 districts each of which elected, by popular vote, a vestry or district board which became the sole sanitary authority for the locality. And each of these new authorities was required to appoint a medical officer of health to advise on the maintenance of health and the prevention of disease among the inhabitants. This provision came from Simon whose experiences in the City had convinced him that if the task of sanitary reform was to be advanced it must be led at the local level by a medical man.

The wording of the clause making this requirement was similar to that of the City Sewers Act under which Simon had been appointed in that no reference was made to the necessity for seeking the approval of the appointment or of the salary by the central government department. There was one other provision which was new and which was to be important in the long run. The vestries and boards were empowered to remove the medical officer of health at their pleasure. This was to cause much heart-burning among the medical officers concerned for many years afterwards.

Politically, the clause making these appointments obligatory was an insignificant one in the context of a bill that was to revolutionise local government in the capital, and it aroused little comment in the Commons. Only one member is on record as taking exception to the idea on the grounds that 'manufacturers and others would be put at the mercy of medical men – perhaps even troublesome ones'. He spoke more truly than he knew.

The newspapers had plenty to say about the bill in general, but only *The Times* picked out the 'health officer' clause as meriting a special reference. It began with a tribute to Simon for the sanitary improvements he had made in the City and expressed the hope that the appointment of medical officers to all the other districts in London would be no less fruitful.

The only ripple disturbing the smooth reception of the clause came from the medical officers of the Poor Law.

They expressed the hope that the new authorities would be instructed to appoint them as medical officers of health and sent a deputation to see Sir Benjamin Hall, president of the Board, to urge their case. They were met by his disarming comment that 'the great point really is that the authorities shall choose men of eminence and with whom, from their station and reputation, the medical officers of the Poor Law Unions would feel pleasure in acting'. And that was that.

The bill passed into law and shortly after, the General Board issued a note of instructions advising the authorities on the appointment and duties of medical officers of health. It recommended that the appointments should be made full-time and that the remuneration should be sufficient to enable the officer to dispense with income derived from private practice. Nevertheless, it said, the holders of these posts should not be debarred from holding any other public appointments nor from work in the hospital or medical school.

The Lancet had supported the clause and the general terms of the appointment, but, with surprising foresight, it opposed full-time appointments on the grounds that exclusion from private practice would make the medical officer a 'specialist'. However, the vestries were urged to make the remuneration sufficient to attract 'men of the highest quality'. The *British Medical Journal*, *The Lancet*'s principal rival, maintained an air of aloofness about the entire proposal. Sanitation seemed not to be its concern.

Following the passing of the act the new authorities accepted their new sanitary responsibilities, for the most part without great enthusiasm but rather in the knowledge that they must obey the law. Forty-eight posts were advertised (two districts were to have two medical officers), at salaries mostly ranging from £40 to £400 a year. Eight districts offered the lower figure and only one (St Marylebone) the higher one. The total salary bill for the 48 medical officers who were to serve a population of three million people was £7,300 a year. Certainly the new authorities could not have been accused of squandering public money on the public health.

Although several vestries saw the desirability of making full-time appointments, most felt that it would not be possible to attract a good man at the salary they professed themselves able to afford. Despite the vague wording of some of the advertisements none of this first generation of medical officers in London was excluded from private practice. Whatever opinions there may have been regarding the size of the salaries, there was no shortage of applicants; most vestries received between 12 and 30 applications. It seems that the vestries took their responsibility for appointing the best men they could get for their money quite seriously. Apart from a few who showed a bias towards a local candidate, the selection was generally made on merit.

What kind of men were appointed to these posts? *The Lancet* described them as 'men who did honour to their profession'. Most of them were young men between 25 and 35; many held junior appointments in the London hospitals and some were lecturers in the medical schools. Just such a man was Simon when he took up his post in the City. It is not unlikely that the vestries were influenced by so successful a precedent. (See appendix A.)

Many of these men were afterwards to achieve distinction in their profession. To mention but a few: John Burdon-Sanderson (Paddington) became regius professor of medicine at Oxford and was subsequently knighted; Frederick Pavy of St Luke's became well known both as a physician and physiologist; John Bristowe (Camberwell) became eminent as a pathologist and senior physician at St Thomas's; George Buchanan (St Giles) became principal medical officer of the local government board and was also knighted; William Odling (Lambeth) became a leading authority on the chemistry of food and water; Edwin Lankester (St James) made notable contributions in many fields of natural science. At least six of them became Fellows of the Royal Society. It is to be doubted whether in any other group of medical men at that time, so high a proportion won such distinction.

The reasons which prompted young men of such promise to take up these new and untried posts can only be guessed.

Possibly, some were interested in securing an assured income, small as it was. Simon reveals in his 'Personal recollections' how opportune in his case was this new source of income. Prestige may also have been a factor. Simon had quickly won for himself a general public esteem such as few medical men had ever before enjoyed. Sir Benjamin Hall's reference to the posts being filled by 'men of eminence' must have given the appointments an added attraction.

Many of these men had already shown an interest in sanitary science; some had taken part in cholera investigations; others had taken the lead in promoting sanitary action in their own parishes. Many had published papers which had shown their acceptance of the sanitary idea and of the paramount importance of environmental measures in the prevention of zymotic diseases. Yet beyond this, a study of the reports of many of them suggests that they were moved by a desire to alleviate the wretched conditions in which so many of the poor lived, and died. One discovers more than a touch of special pleading in their references to poverty, which indicates that humanitarian feeling was a strong motive influencing the actions of the first medical officers of health in London.

As we read their reports, we find much similarity between them in the nature of the work they undertook. This is understandable since the cleansing of a filthy city and the provision of basic sanitary necessities for its inhabitants were mammoth tasks which monopolised the attention of the medical officers for many years to come. Sewers, water supplies and the abatement of gross insanitary nuisances and overcrowding were their daily stock in trade. In all this they had to combat the obstruction and opposition of private interests.

As Dr T Hunt, MOH for St Giles, put it, 'The medical officer of health can never become popular; his functions bring him into constant collision with the apparent interests of many influential persons'. In a similar vein Dr J Tripe, MOH for Hackney, concluded after several years in office, 'The working of the Metropolis Management Act might be characterised as a war of the community against individuals for the public good'.

There were many complaints of how houses were being built on every available piece of land in London. Dr J Freeman, MOH of Mile End, wrote, 'Bricklayers are spreading the webs and meshes of houses with such fearful rapidity in every direction that people are being gradually confined within narrow prisons only open at the top for the admission of what would be air if it were not smoke'. Dr W Rendle, MOH of St George the Martyr, Southwark, reported that 'Our parish is now almost completely built over' and then gave the following figures for population density in several districts in London:

'In Lewisham there are 2 persons to an acre
In Camberwell there are 13 persons to an acre
In Rotherhithe there are 21 persons to an acre
ALL LONDON 30 persons to an acre
In Newington there are 104 persons to an acre
While we have 184 persons to an acre
And in one part
of the parish 244 persons to an acre.'

Lambeth contained a greater number of inhabited houses than any other district in London, nearly 22,000. At the end of his first year Dr W Odling, the MOH, reported that 'over 1,600 were quite unfit for habitation'.

With bad housing went bad sanitation. Thus, Dr J Bristowe (Camberwell) commented 'Of all the abominations which disgrace and pollute the dwellings of the poor, the imperfect, rarely emptied and overflowing cesspools are by far the worst. ... They not merely poison the atmosphere without, but pour their emanations constantly, silently, and deadly into the interior of the houses themselves.'

Bad sanitation was inevitably linked with unwholesome water supplies. In 1856, Dr Odling declared that 'the shallow well waters of London combine the worst features – they represent the drainage of a great manure bed'.

But perhaps the worst of the evils brought to light most consistently in these reports was overcrowding. Every one of them refers to it. 'The main cause,' wrote Dr C Evans (Strand), 'to which we must attribute the high mortality is the close packing and overcrowding which exists throughout the district. . . . Overcrowding and disease mutually act and react upon each other.'

So great was the demand for accommodation of any kind that many thousands of basement cellars were occupied by whole families. The occupation of these cellars had already been made illegal and the prohibition was reinforced in the Metropolis Act of 1855. Nevertheless in 1858 Dr Hunt reported, 'The profit derived from letting the basements of these houses as dwellings is too strong a temptation for their owners and many of the kitchens are let again as soon as the inspector has reported them emptied'.

By this time, London had become the greatest manufacturing city in the world, and great volumes of smoke belched from the numerous factories and workshops, polluting the atmosphere around them. Worst of all were the 'noxious vapours' proceeding from the various processes involved in the so-called 'offensive trades'. In 1857, Dr W Murdock (Rotherhithe) reported 'In the mile length of Rotherhithe High Street there are no less than nine factories for the fabrication of patent manure; that is to say, nine sources of foetid gases. The process gives out a stench which brings about headache, nausea and vomiting among those within its reach and many complaints have been made by the inhabitants.'

There were slaughterhouses in every parish and district. Dr T Hillier (MOH St Pancras) wrote 'There are too many slaughterhouses in crowded districts. It is impossible that slaughtering of animals can be carried on amongst the dense population without proving more or less injurious to the public health. This it does in several ways – by occasioning the escape of effluvia from decomposed animal refuse to the air and along the drains, and by the numerous trades to which it gives rise in the neighbourhood which are offensive and obnoxious such as gut-spinning, tallow-melting, bladder-blowing and paunch-cleansing.'

Dr Evans, reporting on the Strand district in 1856, wrote 'There are nuisances arising from various branches of industry, the slaughtering of sheep and calves in the back-yards and even in the cellars and kitchens, and the keeping of cows in the basements under private dwelling houses; conditions which contrive to exist in the most crowded parts of this district.'

Street accidents are not a new problem. This extract is taken from the annual report for 1864 of Dr Edwin Lankester, the medical officer of health for the vestry of St James's, Westminster. His district included Oxford Street, Regent Street, and Piccadilly.

'My attention has been drawn to the great increase of street accidents, in this and other Parishes with large thoroughfares, in the Metropolis. The number of street accidents causing death last year in London, was upwards of 250. At one hospital where I made inquiry I found that where they had one death, they had 50 patients suffering from the same class of accidents. This gives the enormous number of 12,500 persons suffering from this cause every year in London. I think three things might be done, to diminish this awful amount of death and suffering.

1. In our crowded thoroughfares bridges for foot-passengers might be erected, which would enable them to avoid passing between the vehicles. Such structures should be ornamental. Their base might be connected with public urinals, and they might be constructed at a small expense.

2. A law might be passed, forbidding carriages to go over foot crossings, or turn round corners, otherwise than at a walking pace.

3. The opening up of side streets, and the widening of those which exist, in the neighbourhood of all our great thoroughfares.

I leave these suggestions for your thought and approval.'

More than once a medical officer is found introducing a strong moral tone in reporting to his local board. For example, Dr J Liddle of Whitechapel wrote 'I have in my report, as in duty bound, spoken plainly; if in the opinion of some members of the Board too plainly, my apology is – the deep sense I entertain of the importance of sanitary progress;

for upon the success that shall attend the labours of those engaged in this most sacred cause depends the improvement of the social, moral and intellectual condition of the people'.

Liddle was also among those who saw, as Chadwick had already seen, that sickness among the people imposes a heavy financial burden on the community: 'It cannot be too often impressed upon our minds that sickness among the poor is the great cause of pressure upon the rates; and everything that will tend to diminish the number of sick will be so much saved to the ratepayers'. And later he wrote, 'In the course of time the public will learn that sickness with its concomitant evils – loss of wages, calls upon clubs and friendly societies, the increased amount of charitable contributions, a heavier poor rate – entails more expense upon the community than would be required to carry out sanitary improvements, in widening streets and in erecting more commodious houses for the poor'. Dr R Barnes of Shoreditch underlined this when he wrote in 1856 'To communities as well as to individuals there is nothing so expensive, so fatal to prosperity, as sickness. To a productive and labouring community health is the chief estate.'

These then were the problems which confronted these 48 medical officers, and these extracts from their reports reflect the spirit in which they set out to tackle them. Each worked out his programme of action for his own district, but there is little doubt that the ordering of their activities owed much to the pattern that had already been set by Simon in the City. Indeed it is not unlikely that the reprint of his first five reports which he had had published provided them with a guide for their own programmes.

And what did all their efforts add up to? In January 1857 *The Lancet* calculated that 'in a very modest computation, the number of nuisances that have been either reformed or altogether removed during the past year amounts to upwards of 15,000'. No small achievement!

Later in the same year *The Lancet* devoted an editorial to a review of the work of the metropolitan medical officers. It said 'Traps have been laid to catch all kinds of stench and snares set to abate all forms of nuisance; offensive slaughterhouses have been removed and ruinous tenements healthily rebuilt. The milk has been robbed of a portion of its water and the dirty children in the alleys more plentifully supplied. Dustmen have been reluctantly obliged to remove refuse and agonised manufacturers compelled to consume their own smoke.' An eloquent testimony to the endeavours of these pioneers of public health in the capital city.

Their reports show that, in general, relationships between the vestries and their medical officers were good. A testimony to this is the fact that after making allowance for posts subsequently made redundant by the amalgamation of small districts, all but five posts were still held in 1866 by the same men who had been appointed in 1856. Of the five officers who had been replaced, three had died, one had resigned and one had emigrated. Several served their districts for over 30 years and Dr J Bristowe died in 1895 after 40 years as medical officer of health for Camberwell.

We must now turn back to a very important step that was taken by the metropolitan medical officers shortly after entering on their new careers. They soon realised that it would be advantageous to all of them if they could meet together to discuss their common problems. (See appendix B.) Thus it was that on 23 April 1856 Dr Pavy (St Lukes) invited seven of his colleagues to a meeting which was held at his house, 3 Finsbury Square, at which the formation of an association was discussed. They decided to proceed by convening a meeting to which all their colleagues would be invited. This meeting was held on 13 May at the rooms of the Medical Society of London, 32a George Street, Hanover Square, when 30 medical officers attended.

During the proceedings Dr Lankester (St James) put forward the proposition

'That the Medical Officers of Health here present combine themselves into an Association for the purpose of mutual assistance and to the establishment of such a plan of action in their several districts as may best conduce to the efficiency of sanitary administration and to the advancement of sanitary science.'

Some members objected to the words 'combine themselves' as being likely to misinterpretation; perhaps it was redolent of the Combination Acts of the past. After further discussion, Dr Lankester and his seconder Dr Aldis (St George) agreed to modify and shorten their proposal, which then read as follows:

> 'That the Medical Officers of Health present form themselves into an Association for the purpose of mutual assistance and the advancement of sanitary science.'

Immediately following the passing of the proposition creating the association, Dr Bristowe proposed 'that Mr Simon be requested to act as President of the Association'. The minute book records that 'A short discussion arose as to the policy of uniting themselves with any officers of the Government and a fear was expressed lest any of the Vestries should suspect anything like a political combination on the part of their Medical Officers; but it was ultimately agreed that they had nothing to do with Mr Simon politically but as a man of Sanitary Science, and there was no difference of opinion as to the great advantage that would be gained by having such a person as he as their President, it was then carried unanimously'. Thus Simon became the first president and in his neat, clear, firm hand he signed the minutes of this first meeting.

All but two of the 48 men joined the association. Dr Griffiths of Clerkenwell seems to have been a somewhat eccentric person who preferred to go his own way alone. Despite several invitations to join he remained aloof and retained his post for 40 years. In the case of Dr Letherby who had succeeded Simon in the City, the reason for not joining was probably different. The City was excepted from the area of the metropolis in the 1855 act and had appointed Simon under its own act. Letherby presumably considered that he was not one of the 'metropolitan' medical officers for whom the association was formed.

In 1856 there was only a handful of medical officers of health outside the metropolitan area and over time most of them applied to join the association. From 1859 they were allowed to join as honorary members and before long they outnumbered the metropolitan members themselves. In 1860, after a postal ballot, honorary membership was also granted to Dr T Southwood-Smith, Dr Henry Rumsey and Dr William Farr, and in 1861 to Dr Greenhow and to Dr Edward Seaton, both of whom were friends and colleagues of Simon. In 1862, the name of Dr Duncan of Liverpool was added to the roll of honorary members along with Major Graham, the Registrar General and, most significant of all, Edwin Chadwick.

An early decision of the association was to set up four standing committees to investigate and report on special problems. Their subjects were trade nuisances in relation to health and the means of obviating them; food adulteration; the causes of diseases, epidemic, endemic and contagious; and meteorology.

During the early years various aspects of these subjects were considered at the meetings of the association. Much time was also devoted to the domestic affairs and management of the association and to drafting its constitution. Sometimes matters of more direct concern to the medical officers called for attention. For example, at the meeting held in April 1858, the chief business was a discussion on the salaries of medical officers of health. 'Dr Hillier reported that the Vestry of St Pancras had reduced his salary from £400 to £250, forty voting for and twenty-six against the resolution. It was suggested in debate that it was possibly more "politic" to accept the reduction lest a worse evil – dismissal – ensued.' This was by no means the only time that this problem was to be brought before the association. There was little that the association could do about it save to give their unfortunate colleagues their moral support.

Simon was a staunch ally of the association. He contributed freely to discussions and from time to time he gave previews of drafts of government circulars. He also arranged for the association to have the use of the boardroom at the General Board of Health as a venue for their meetings. Sir Benjamin Hall, the president of the Board, wrote giving his formal permission, saying that he had 'confident hopes that their consultations and combined exertions may lead to beneficial results in sanitary science and materially promote the ends for which this department is maintained'.

These hopes were already being fulfilled and thus it was that under the combined surveillance of these 48 men London became the proving ground both of the medical officers of health and also of the programme of sanitary advance of which they were both pioneers and leaders.

3

John Snow

*The Broad Street pump and after**

On 19 June 1858, the following notice appeared among the announcements of deaths in *The Times*: 'On the 16th inst., at his residence 18 Sackville Street, Piccadilly, John Snow, M.D., of apoplexy, aged 45.' For some weeks prior to his last illness Snow had been working on his book *On Chloroform and Other Anaesthetics*. According to his friend Benjamin Ward Richardson, he was drafting the concluding paragraph and was actually writing the word 'exit' when he was seized with a stroke from which he died ten days later.

It was nine years before his untimely death that Snow had first put forward his theory concerning the spread of cholera by polluted water. This he did in a small pamphlet of about 30 pages which was published at his own expense. But this first essay in the field of infectious diseases received only scant attention at the time. Five years later, in 1854, when cholera was sweeping across the country for the third time, he carried out his classic researches in South London. This investigation, which remains to this day a model of scientific inquiry, established beyond all reasonable doubt that cholera is a water-borne disease. Snow incorporated the substantial body of new evidence which he had gathered in the course of this inquiry into his 'much enlarged' volume of 162 pages – the so-called 'second edition' of his book *On the Mode of Transmission of Cholera* which was published early in 1855. In the next three years only 56 copies of the book were sold, and in return for an outlay of £200 incurred in its preparation, the author was reimbursed with the princely sum of £3 12s. 0d.

Snow's theory ran counter to the prevailing view of his

---

* Reprinted from *The Medical Officer* (1958) 99:347–9.

time, which attributed infectious diseases like cholera to the effluvia arising from filth and putrefaction. It is hardly to be wondered, therefore, that at first there were few who were disposed to accept this new explanation. In 1849, a reviewer commenting in *The Lancet* on Snow's first pamphlet on cholera wrote, 'The arguments adduced by the author against emanations causing the disease are not by any means conclusive'. Following the cholera epidemic of 1853–4, the Royal College of Physicians set up an investigation into its causes under Drs William Baly and William Gull. They considered Snow's thesis and rejected it outright. 'The theory as a whole is untenable,' they reported and added, 'The matter which is the cause of cholera increases and finds the conditions for its action under the influence of foul or damp air.' So, too, the medical inspectors appointed by the General Board of Health in 1854 to inquire into the Soho outbreak, having examined Snow's views upon it, commented, 'we see no reason to adopt this belief'. The principal objections raised against Snow's theory were that it did not account either for the sudden onset or for the decline of the epidemics as satisfactorily as the current explanation in terms of miasmata.

In 1856, John Snow visited Paris with his uncle, Mr Empson, of Bath. Empson, a dealer in curios, was known personally to the Emperor and Ward Richardson records that 'on this occasion special imperial favours were shown to him in which the nephew participated'. While in Paris, Snow entered his book at the Institut de France for a prize which was offered for the most outstanding contribution towards the prevention or treatment of cholera. Ward Richardson reports that no notice was taken of Snow's researches by the Institute. On the other hand Sir D'Arcy Power, the medical historian, writing of Snow in the *Dictionary of National Biography*, states that 'his essay upon the mode of communication of cholera which was first published in 1849 was awarded by the Institute of France a prize of £1,200'. In reply to a recent inquiry made by the writer, M Pierre Gauja, the present archivist of the Institute, confirmed that Snow did not in fact receive this award. It would appear that his theory was no more acceptable abroad than at home, for about the same time Max Pettenkofer in Germany also rejected it.

In England two men of note, William Budd and William Farr, were almost alone in voicing their approval of Snow's thesis during his lifetime. In 1849, shortly after Snow had published his first paper on cholera, Budd brought out a pamphlet of his own on the same subject. He put forward a theory of causation and transmission of the disease similar to that of Snow, but in doing so he made a full acknowledgement of the priority of Snow's published work. In all his subsequent writings on cholera Budd stressed the water-borne nature of the disease and was at pains to give full credit to Snow for having first made this discovery.

William Farr at the General Register Office gave a more qualified support to Snow's theory. He himself had noted the high mortality from cholera which occurred in those districts of London whose water supplies were drawn directly from the sewage-laden reaches of the Thames. In the Report of the Registrar General for 1852 he discussed Snow's findings and reached the conclusion that the facts 'lend some countenance to Dr Snow's theory'. Four years later, in his letter to the Registrar General, Farr presented a long and detailed statistical account of the cholera epidemic of 1853–4. He concluded as follows: 'It is right to state that Dr Snow by his hypothesis and researches and by his personal inquiries; that the Registrar General by procuring information and by promoting inquiry; as well as the Board of Health by the Report, have all contributed in various ways to establish the fact that the cholera-matter, or cholerine, when it is most fatal, is largely diffused through water as well as through other channels'.

The report to which Farr referred was that made to the president of the General Board of Health by John Simon, in which he expressed the cautious view that 'fecalised drinking water and fecalised air equally may breed and convey the poison'. Simon remained for long an adherent of the old theory of the miasmata, and his acceptance of Snow's thesis came only gradually and after many years. In the month of

Snow's death in 1858 he referred to his 'peculiar doctrine as to the contagiousness of cholera' and commented somewhat patronisingly that 'whatever may be the worth of the theory, it has been of use in contributing to draw attention to the vast hygienic importance of a pure water supply'. Sixteen years later he had moved his position, and in a report to the Local Government Board he remarked, 'Indeed, with regard to the manner of spread of the enterozymotic diseases generally, it deserves notice that the whole pathological argument which I am explaining grew amongst us in this country out of the very cogent facts which our cholera epidemics supplied, and to which the late Dr Snow 25 years ago had the merit of forcing medical attention, an attention at first quite incredulous, but which at least for the last 15 years as facts have accumulated has gradually been changing into conviction.' Later still in 1890, in his *English Sanitary Institutions*, Simon, looking back over the years to Snow's discovery, could write that it 'may probably still be counted the most important truth yet acquired by medical science for the prevention of epidemics of cholera.' This appreciation of Snow's work was handsome if somewhat belated.

The 30 years which followed the publication of Snow's book witnessed a plethora of new books on the subject of cholera. A perusal of 12 of these volumes disclosed no mention at all of Snow in six of them (Johnson, 1855; Jameson, 1855; Shrimpton, 1866; Jencken, 1867; Parkes, 1873; Macpherson, 1884). Chapman (1866) rejected Snow's 'far-fetched doctrine', Bellew (1855) found it 'untenable', as did Boyd Mushet (1885). Only three of these writers expressed their agreement with Snow's conclusions: Macnamara (1872), Blanc (1873) and Wendt (1885). These examples indicate how tardy and gradual was the general acceptance of Snow's theory.

In 1884 Koch announced his discovery of the cholera vibrio to the Berlin Conference and ten years later an English translation of his papers on cholera was published in this country. Koch made no mention of Snow although he fully accepted the water-borne nature of the disease. William Gairdner, Professor of Medicine at Glasgow, contributed an introduction to the English edition in which he paid a fitting tribute to John Snow:

'Since Dr Snow's researches were published and adopted by the Registrar General in England there has never been much doubt among us as to the water-communication of the choleraic infection, the evidence of which seemed to go on accumulating as the incidence of the disease, in respect of particular places, was more and more studied, and the severity of local epidemics was found to be strictly in accordance with the presence of dangerous impurities in the water supply.'

The discoveries of the bacteriologists finally dethroned the doctrine of emanations, and served both to underline the soundness of John Snow's observations and to confirm the truth of his deductions.

THE BROAD STREET PUMP

The name of John Snow is invariably associated with the Broad Street pump and with the outbreak of cholera which centred upon it. The story of this old pump forms an interesting chapter in the history of public health. Just when it was set up in Broad Street is not known. The houses in this part of Soho were built between 1700 and 1740 and it is likely that the well was sunk about the same time. The district was a suitable one for shallow wells, for water could be obtained at a depth of about 20 feet almost everywhere. As a result wells were plentiful. There were at least 12 pumps within a radius of a quarter of a mile of Broad Street.

By 1850 two private companies – the New River and the Grand Junction – were supplying piped water to all the houses in the area. At that time these supplies were intermittent, the water being turned on for about two hours daily except on Sundays. Each household had to install a butt or cistern which was filled whenever the main supply became available. These storage butts were notoriously bad. They were usually uncovered, rarely if ever cleaned, and as a result the water drawn from them was generally dirty and often unsavoury.

By contrast the water from the well in Broad Street was clear, bright, and sparkling, albeit through the presence of carbonic acid and nitrates, the end-products of organic contamination. Throughout the district around Golden Square its waters, always available and invariably cool and palatable, were most highly regarded. Not only did house-holders close at hand make extensive use of it, but many people living at a distance preferred to draw their water from Broad Street in preference to their local wells. It was commonly the duty of the children to fetch the water from the pump, and old people living alone bemoaned the fact that they had no one to fetch water for them. The pump-handle had a ladle attached to it from which the children were accustomed to drink, although we know that some parents disapproved of this practice. Many of the small workshops in the locality kept butts filled with the well water to be used for drinking purposes, especially in summer. The water was also used for mixing with spirits in all the taverns round about and it was supplied to customers in the coffee-shops and dining-rooms in the area. Some of the little shops used to bottle the water, add a little effervescent powder and sell it as 'sherbet' drink.

Perhaps the most striking testimony to the attractions of this water comes from Snow's account of the widow of Hampstead. This lady, whose husband had formerly owned the percussion-cap factory in Broad Street, had a bottle of the well water brought to her by a cart which travelled each day to St James. This was to prove her undoing, for in the cholera epidemic she alone of the inhabitants of Hampstead contracted the disease and died.

The month of August, 1854, was hot and dry and when cholera broke out in Broad Street it spread through the little neighbourhood like fire in a rickyard. Within ten days the population was literally decimated. It was without doubt, as John Snow himself described it, 'the most terrible outbreak of cholera which ever occurred in this kingdom'. At the time Snow was living in Sackville Street, about half a mile from the affected area, and although he was already fully engaged in his investigation in South London he hastened to the scene of this new outbreak. His suspicions quickly fell on the well in Broad Street and these were strengthened when he discovered that 'nearly all the deaths had taken place within a short distance of the pump'. He was able to establish that almost all the people who had died had consumed water from the pump. After pursuing his inquiries further, Snow recorded, 'I had an interview with the Board of Guardians of St James's parish on the evening of Thursday, 7th September, and represented the above circumstances to them. In consequence of what I said the handle of the pump was removed on the following day.'

It is interesting to note that the minutes of the board of guardians and of the vestry contain no reference to Snow's intervention. It is probable that he made his representation to the sanitary committee which had been set up by the guardians to act during the epidemic, and that it was this body which ordered the pump to be taken out of use. By the morning of 8 September the epidemic had already declined sharply and the closure of the well did little to affect its course, although it may well have prevented a fresh outbreak. The removal of the handle was not by any means the end of the Broad Street pump, for within a short time it was brought back into service again.

Two further associates of John Snow enter the story at this stage – one a doctor and the other a clergyman. The doctor was Edwin Lankester, who in the following year became the first medical officer of health of St James; the clergyman was Henry Whitehead, the young curate at St Luke's church in Berwick Street. Lankester was a member of the vestry and at his instigation a local inquiry into the epidemic was ordered to be carried out at the expense of the parish. Both John Snow and Henry Whitehead were co-opted on to the committee which was set up for this purpose. It was in the course of this investigation that Whitehead made the discovery which had till then eluded Snow and which brought a triumphant confirmation of his hypothesis. This was the elucidation of the way in which the well had become polluted.

Whitehead discovered that a baby living at 40 Broad

Street, the nearest house to the pump, had died from what was described as 'exhaustion following diarrhoea' and that the child's illness immediately preceded the onset of the cholera epidemic. From his inquiries at the house he learnt that the baby's discharges had been disposed of into a cesspool which was less than three feet from the well. An immediate inspection revealed conspicuous evidence of the percolation of faecal matter from the ill constructed cesspool through the decaying brickwork which lined the well. The chain of evidence incriminating the pump was now complete. Yet even this disclosure did not secure its final removal. Instead, the well was closed for six weeks while the brickwork was renewed, it was then pumped out completely three times, after which it was opened for use by the public once more.

In the following year, 1856, Edwin Lankester was appointed medical officer of health of St James's parish under the Metropolis Management Act. One of the first matters to which he gave his attention was the water supply of the district. It was his aim to get rid of the numerous shallow wells in the area, and in his first annual report to the vestry he complained that 'the most impure water in the parish is that of the Broad Street pump, and it is altogether the most popular'. This comment is all the more striking when it is recalled that it was made within two years of the great epidemic. Lankester went on to report that a chemical analysis had revealed that this water contained more inorganic salts (chlorides and nitrates) derived from organic pollution, than the common sewer.

The vestry appear to have been unmoved by these revelations, so in the following year Lankester wrote to every one of his fellow medical officers of health in the metropolitan area asking their opinions about surface wells. Their replies, which he published in full, showed that the general consensus of opinion was in favour of closure. This seems to have led to a minor victory, for at the beginning of 1858 all the shallow wells in the parish were closed by order of the vestry. Lankester's success was short-lived, however, for in his report for that year he grumbled 'You did not think it advisable to continue the closing of the pumps'. And so, after an interval of four months all the wells were in use again.

Four years later Lankester took up the cudgels once more. In his customary forthright manner he informed the vestry that all the wells in the parish were unsafe, with the single exception of the artesian near the church in Piccadilly. He reminded them that St James was now lagging behind most other districts for 'with the exception of our own parish these surface well-pumps have nearly all been closed throughout London'. He spoke of 'offering the public the filtered sewage of these pumps'. This seems to have prompted the vestry to take some action, for in 1864 Lankester was able to report that 'the wells in the parish are gradually being abandoned – seven only remain'. But the Broad Street pump was among them. He remarked that drinking fountains had largely replaced wells in popular esteem but that St James had fewer of them than any other London parish.

It was in the next year that the threat of cholera returned to this country once again. Lankester thereupon urged the vestry to lock the remaining pumps as a safety precaution, reminding them of the part that impure water, especially from surface wells, had played in the spread of cholera in the past. His warning went unheeded. The threatened outbreak materialised in the summer of 1866 when cholera broke out in the teeming slums of East London. Lankester promptly submitted to the vestry a special report on the state of the wells which still remained in service in the area. This revealed abundant chemical evidence of organic contamination and once again he drew special attention to the Broad Street pump. Further support now came from another and perhaps unexpected source, for on 31 July a letter headed 'The Broad Street pump' appeared in *The Times*. Signed by Dr W Allen Miller, of King's College Hospital, and Prof E Frankland, of the Royal College of Chemistry, it deplored the fact that the old pump was still in use and commented on the unfitness of its waters. The writers concluded with a solemn warning that the whole area could be infected 'by a single case of cholera occurring within the drainage area of the pump'.

Three days later a case of cholera was reported in No 30 Broad Street. Lankester now sounded a note of alarm. He warned the vestry yet again of the dangers of spreading the disease through the pollution of water; 'this can occur in no other way than by our pumps'. He pronounced the wells to be dangerous. 'I dare not take the responsibility of remaining quiet while these pumps are open, and, at the risk of offending you by my pertinacity, I implore you to order the pumps to be shut.'

This appeal seems to have been successful in bringing about, at long last, the final closure of the Broad Street pump. There are no further references to its use from that time.

Edwin Lankester died in 1874 and was succeeded as medical officer of health by James Edmunds. In his annual report for 1884, eight wells were mentioned by name, including the one in Broad Street which was said 'to have been covered but not filled in'. The rest is silence. Broad Street remained but its pump had passed into history.

Today, 100 years after the death of John Snow, the student of public health can still visit many of the places associated with his career. Bateman's Buildings, the little back street in Soho, where in 1836 Snow rented a room following his long walk to London to study medicine; Great Windmill Street, where a plaque on the wall of the Lyric Theatre marks the site of the Hunterian School of Medicine in which Snow was a student from 1836–8; Frith Street, Soho, were in 1838 he 'nailed up his colours' and started his first practice; 18 Sackville Street which was his home from 1852 until his death, and Brompton Cemetery, where stands a replica of the original monument erected to his memory by his friends. But perhaps it is fitting that the pilgrimage should end in Broad Street – now Broadwick Street, W1 – and at the old tavern which three years ago was renamed in honour of John Snow. For, below the inn-sign which bears his portrait, a tablet on the wall draws the attention of the passer-by to a red granite stone at the kerbside. This stone marks the site of the Broad Street pump.

BIBLIOGRAPHY

The following are the principal sources which were used in the preparation of this article:

Annual reports of the medical officer of health. St James, Westminster, 1856 to 1884.

Annual reports, registrar general. London, 1848 to 1856.

Budd W. Malignant cholera. London, 1849.

Chave SPW. John Snow and cholera in London. London School of Hygiene Library, 1955.

Chave SPW. Henry Whitehead and cholera in Broad Street. Medical History, 1958, 2, pp 92–108. (*See chapter 4*)

Koch R. On the bacteriological diagnosis of cholera and other papers. Translated G Duncan. Edinburgh, 1894.

Reports on epidemic cholera. London, Royal College of Physicians, 1854.

Report of the Medical Council in relation to epidemic-cholera of 1854. London, General Board of Health, 1855.

Report on the cholera outbreak in St James, Westminster, 1854. London, Cholera Inquiry Committee, St James's Vestry, 1855.

Report on the London cholera epidemics of 1848–9 and 1853–4, by the Medical Officer to the Board. London, General Board of Health, 1856.

Richardson BW. John Snow, MD. The Asclepiad, 4, London, 1887.

Snow John. On the mode of communication of cholera (2nd edition). London, 1855.

4

Henry Whitehead
and cholera in Broad Street*

The cholera epidemic in the St James's district of Westminster
in 1854 was perhaps the most terrible outbreak of that disease
which this country has ever known – terrible because of its
virulence and local concentration. More than 500 people who
lived or worked within an area only a few hundred yards
square died of the disease in ten days. The outbreak is
memorable, too, in the annals of epidemiology because of its
association with John Snow's historic investigation into
the Broad Street pump. Less well known, however, is
the important contribution made by the Reverend Henry
Whitehead, but it was, in fact, his work which constituted
the first independent confirmation of Snow's hypothesis
attributing the spread of cholera to contaminated water.

At the time of the epidemic, Whitehead, then aged 29,
was serving his first curacy at St Luke's Berwick Street,
the parish which included Broad Street and its environs.
Throughout the dreadful days which followed the explosion
of the outbreak on 1 September, the young curate worked
incessantly to bring help and comfort to the afflicted and
bereaved.

John Snow was busily engaged too, but in another way.
His home in Sackville Street, Piccadilly, was little more than
ten minutes walking distance from Berwick Street. Although
he was already conducting an investigation into cholera
in South London, he hastened to the scene of this new
outburst. Having surveyed the local circumstances, his
suspicions fell upon the 'much-frequented' pump in Broad
Street.[1] It appeared to him 'that there was no other circum-
stance or agent common to the circumscribed locality in
which the sudden increase of cholera occurred'. He obtained

---

* Reprinted from *Medical History* (1958), 2:92–108.

the addresses of the 89 fatal cases which occurred at the onset
of the epidemic from the General Register Office and made
detailed inquiries into each one. He reported, 'I found that
nearly all the deaths had taken place within a short distance
of the pump', and, further, he was able to establish that at
least 69 of these people had drunk water from it. On the
evening of 7 September he put forward his views to a
committee of the board of guardians, and although they were
quite incredulous they ordered the pump-handle to be
removed on the following morning.

The epidemic steadily declined, and when, by mid-
September, the yellow flags which had given warning of the
pestilence were removed from the streets, a newspaper
correspondent entered the area and gave the following
description of the aftermath of the visitation:[2]

'The outbreak of cholera in the vicinity of Golden Square
is now subsiding, but the passenger through the streets
which compass that district will see many evidences of
the alarming severity of the attack. Men and women in
mourning are to be found in great numbers, and the chief
topic of conversation is the recent epidemic. The shop
windows are filled with placards relating to the subject. At
every turn the instructions of the new Board of Health
stare you in the face. In shop windows, on church and
chapel doors, on dead walls, and at every available point
appear parochial hand-bills directing the poor where to
apply for gratuitous relief. An oil shop puts forth a large
cask at its door, labelled in gigantic capitals 'Chloride of
Lime'. The most remarkable evidence of all, however, and
the most important, consists in the continual presence of
lime in the roadways. The puddles are white and milky
with it, the stones are smeared with it; great splashes of
it lie about in the gutters, and the air is redolent with
its strong and not very agreeable odour. The parish
authorities have very wisely determined to wash all the
streets of the tainted district with this powerful disinfec-
tant; accordingly the purification takes place regularly
every evening. The shopkeepers have dismal stories to tell

– how they would hear in the evening that one of their neighbours whom they had been talking with in the morning had expired after a few hours of agony and torture. It has even been asserted that the number of corpses was so great that they were removed wholesale in dead-carts for want of sufficient hearses to convey them; but let us hope this is incorrect.'

It was not long before stories of dire events which were said to have taken place in the cholera area became current. Many of these reports were exaggerated, and it was in part to provide a corrective that within a few weeks Henry Whitehead published his own account of the epidemic. Entitled *The Cholera in Berwick Street,*[3] it provided a sober and objective report of the outbreak. Although the population of the area was literally decimated, there was, Whitehead said, 'no panic which somewhat surprised me, as I had always heard and read that great pestilences were invariably attended by wholesale demoralisation of the population'. He included in this report mortality figures, which he had compiled himself, for each street in the parish. This pamphlet is of interest in that no particular mention is made either of Broad Street or its pump. Berwick Street, not Broad Street, figured in the title because the parish church was situated there. As to the pump, the removal of the handle would seem to have passed unnoticed by the stricken population. That its waters were in any way connected with the cause of their distress was beyond belief, a view which was, in fact, expressed directly to Snow at the time. Whitehead, it would seem, either had not heard of it, or if he had, did not deem it worthy of mention.

In the period following the outbreak, John Snow was occupied in gathering further evidence in support of his thesis relating the spread of cholera to the waters of the Broad Street pump. At the same time, the medical committee of the General Board of Health carried out a local inquiry on behalf of the government. This was conducted by three medical inspectors appointed for the purpose. In the course of the investigation, attention was paid to the account given by Whitehead, who is described as the 'exemplary and indefatigable curate of St Luke's'.[4] John Snow also submitted his explanation of the outbreak, which was considered by the inspectors and rejected outright. 'After careful inquiry we see no reason to adopt this belief,' they concluded.[5]

In reporting the results of this inquiry to Sir Benjamin Hall, the president of the General Board of Health, John Ayrton Paris, the chairman of the Medical Council, wrote:[6]

'The extraordinary irruption of cholera in the Soho district which was carefully examined by Mr Fraser, Mr Hughes and Mr Ludlow does not appear to afford any exception to generalisations respecting local states of uncleanliness, overcrowding, and imperfect ventilation. The suddenness of the outbreak, its immediate climax and short duration, all point to some atmospheric or other widely diffused agent still to be discovered, and forbid the assumption, in this instance, of any communication of the disease from person to person either by infection or by contamination of water with the excretions of the sick.'

It was at this stage that, at the instigation of Dr Edwin Lankester, the local vestry took action on its own account. At a meeting held on 2 November 1854, Lankester, who was later to become the first medical officer of health for the St James's district, gave notice of the following motion:[7]

'That a Committee of this Vestry be appointed for the purpose of investigating the causes arising out of the present sanitary conditions of the Parish of the late outbreak of cholera in the districts of Golden Square and Berwick Street.'

At the next meeting, held three weeks later, there was some discussion before the motion was agreed to;[8] thereupon a committee consisting of nine vestrymen, including Lankester and the churchwardens, was appointed.

The inquiry had scarcely begun before it met with a serious setback which almost brought the whole venture to an end. On 14 December 1854 the vestry received a communication from the board of guardians of the

Poor of St James's,[9] regretting the setting up of the inquiry,

> 'by reason of the expense that it is likely to entail upon the year's poor rate already wholly unequal to meet the ordinary expenditure, but in greater degree on account of the mischievous effects which a renewed investigation of the subject so recently made by the Government officers is calculated to inflict on the Householders and Inhabitants of the locality, now but slowly recovering from the serious depression of their trade and employment and by whom the inquiry instituted by Vestry is consequently viewed with feelings of dissatisfaction and alarm.'

This gave rise to a motion that the committee should discontinue its work which was only negatived 'after considerable discussion'.

Having thus been reprieved, the committee began by considering all the available documentary evidence, and once again Henry Whitehead's firsthand account proved of value. It was decided that an approach be made to Sir Benjamin Hall to ask for such information concerning the local outbreak as might be available in his department. This request met with a blunt refusal on the grounds that 'investigations of this kind were more valuable when independent'.[10] That this serious rebuff from the government did not deter the committee from continuing with its task may well have been due to the personality of Edwin Lankester. From his writings it is clear that he was not a man who would lightly have abandoned a chosen course of action. His characteristic persistence and doggedness are outstanding features of the series of annual reports which he made to the vestry during his long tenure of office as medical officer of health.

Whether as a result of the leadership of Lankester or not, the committee of inquiry went on with their work. They next set out to obtain the information they needed by circulating a questionnaire to the householders of the district, asking a number of details of their living circumstances. It was not long before they learnt that this is not often a fruitful method of inquiry. 'This measure did not produce the anticipated results,' they reported.[11] The committee, therefore, decided to seek this information by means of personal interviews, and to this end they added eight new members to their number. Among these newcomers were John Snow and Henry Whitehead, who now probably met for the first time. Snow had just completed his book *On Cholera*, which was published in January 1855, and he presented a copy to Whitehead. But, having read it, the young curate remained unconvinced. He wrote to Snow setting out his reasons and stating that, in his opinion, an intensive inquiry would reveal the falsity of the argument attributing the spread of cholera to the Broad Street pump.

Whitehead thereupon determined to carry out such an inquiry himself with the aim either of confirming or refuting the 'Snovian' hypothesis. The investigation which he carried out in the ensuing months in Broad Street was embodied in a report entitled 'Special investigation of Broad Street',[12] which he submitted to the committee in June 1855. When printed subsequently this report covered 42 printed pages. It is a record of a thorough and searching investigation carried out with all the objectivity of a truly scientific inquiry.

Whitehead set out to interview every family which had been resident in Broad Street at the time of the outbreak. A number of these had moved away, but he endeavoured to communicate with them, in some cases travelling 'a considerable distance to do so'. In the case of the residents who remained in Broad Street, Whitehead went over the ground many times, often visiting a family on four or five occasions in order to obtain and confirm the facts that he needed. In respect of every person who had died from cholera he ascertained the name, age, position of the rooms occupied, the sanitary arrangements, the water drunk, with particular regard to the pump, and finally the hour of onset of the fatal attack. He found that the piped water supplied to the district by the two private water companies could be excluded as a factor in the spread of cholera, and confirmed that the only other source of water in common use was the pump.

'Slowly and I may add reluctantly,' reported Whitehead,

the conclusion was reached 'that the use of this water was connected with the commencement and continuance of the outburst'. The steps by which he came round to this view are recounted by him in detail. Of the 56 fatal cases among the residents which occurred between 31 August and 2 September, only two were not shown to have drunk the pump water. Among the 28 non-residents who died of cholera, 24 worked in factories where water from the pump was in constant use.

Whitehead sought the 50 residents who had contracted cholera but had recovered. He discovered that, of these, 35 had consumed the pump water after 30 August, and that 34 were seized during the period 31 August to 2 September. Throughout the investigation Whitehead took account of the residents who had not been attacked. He ascertained that 279 of these had not consumed the water from the pump between the last week of August and the first week of September, but that a further 43 had, in fact, done so. Altogether Whitehead was able to contact personally no less than 497 of the 896 persons who were resident at the time of the outburst. He remarked that he was able to do this because he had collected 'full statistical information throughout the whole of St Luke's district', and was thus dealing with a matter with which he was already fully familiar.

'The ordinary course of my duties taking me almost daily into the street, I was under no necessity to be either hasty or intrusive, but asked my questions just when and where opportunity occurred, making a point of letting scarcely a day pass without acquiring some information and not caring how often I had to verify it in quarters where I could rely upon a willingness to converse upon the subject.'

He concluded that among those who drank the pump water, the ratio of persons attacked to those unaffected was 80:57, whilst the corresponding ratio among the non-drinkers was 20:279. Clearly the case against the pump was a strong one.

Whitehead then went on to add what might be described as a clinical study to his statistical inquiry. He gave a detailed description of the occurrence of cholera in 15 households, in every case of which the evidence clearly implicated the pump. Among these examples Whitehead paid particular attention to the case which Snow had cited as an especially noteworthy piece of evidence in favour of his hypothesis. This concerned the widow of Hampstead. This good lady had a bottle of water from the Broad Street pump delivered to her home each day by a cart which travelled from Soho. She contracted cholera on 1 September and died the next day. A niece from Islington, who visited the old lady and partook of the water also died. No other cases of cholera occurred in the districts in which these women lived. It would appear that some people had expressed the view that the water-bottle had not been filled at the Broad Street pump. Whitehead sought out her sons and confirmed that they themselves had filled the bottle at the fatal pump. Neither Snow nor Whitehead revealed the lady's identity, but she was, in fact, Susannah, the widow of one Eley, who had owned the percussion-cap factory at 38 Broad Street.

The young curate then went on to give a detailed account of several individual cases of cholera 'as an illustration of the manner in which the whole inquiry had been conducted, and as showing very remarkably, the utter worthlessness of hastily collected facts'.

In presenting his findings, Whitehead paid particular attention to instances which appeared to refute Snow's hypothesis, namely, to examples of people who drank the pump water without ill-effect and to others who were stricken without having consumed the suspected water. Concerning the latter, in several instances, persistent inquiry led to the suspicion that the water had, in fact, been consumed. There were also several cases of cholera having been contracted by persons who had been in close attendance upon other sufferers.

Whitehead also discovered that the houses which escaped the disease altogether were those which accommodated considerably fewer than the average number of residents in the houses in the street. These dwellings were found in other respects to be 'the best regulated in respect of their water systems and therefore there was less need for the inmates to resort elsewhere for their water'. Moreover, there were fewer children in these houses; the children were 'the general carriers of the pump water wherever it was habitually used'. This accounted for the relative immunity of the aged and infirm, for they had no one to fetch water for them.

In taking account of the official view that the spread of cholera was in some way connected with the effluvia rising from the drains, Whitehead established that the inhabitants of cellars and kitchens, where the effects of these exhalations were likely to have been most pronounced, had, in fact, suffered less than those living on upper floors. Three women living in kitchens who had died during the epidemic were shown to have washed the linen of cholera patients.

On the assumption that the pump water had contained the cause of the infection, Whitehead attempted to determine the period during which the choleraic agent had been present. He found that he could not assign any cases of cholera to the consumption of pump water after 8 am on 6 September. Referring back to the statistics quoted in his first pamphlet, he noted 'supposing the number of rapid cases assigned to each day may be taken as an index to the malignancy of the cause, . . . there was then a very perceptible decrease . . . after the cause had been in operation somewhat over forty-eight hours'. The day of greatest pollution was 31 August, and he concluded that partial purification must have occurred by 3 September; he mentioned that he himself had drunk a little of the water with some brandy on that day. But in regard to this he uttered a timely warning, 'I trust that no-one will be for settling these questions by single instances'.

What is perhaps the most interesting part of Whitehead's investigation was his discovery of the way in which the well-water became polluted. 'The possibility of the water having been contaminated by matter thrown off from a cholera patient, who might, so to speak, have imported the disease from another locality had often been discussed in committee,' but no evidence was forthcoming to support this contention. Whitehead made this discovery after he had reached the end of his inquiry and prepared his report. In a typically modest understatement, the young curate wrote:[13]

'One day last week, however, I happened to be studying the Registrar's Returns (of deaths) for a purpose un-connected with this matter, when my eye fell upon the following entry:
"At 40, Broad Street, 2nd September, a daughter, aged five months, exhaustion after an attack of Diarrhoea four days previous to death."

He had, in fact, known of this case much earlier, but had passed it over because it concerned an infant. It was only now that he appreciated its possible double significance; first it had occurred in the house nearest the pump, and secondly the child's attack antedated the violent outbreak by about 48 hours.

He was that day (3 April 1855) about to present his report to the committee. Before doing so, he hastened to the house and interviewed the dead child's mother. The poor woman lived in the back room on the ground floor of No 40, and had lost both her child and her husband, a policeman, in the late epidemic. In answer to Whitehead's questions, she described how, during her baby's illness, she had steeped its soiled napkins in pails of water and had emptied some of these into the cesspool at the front of the house. The account continued: 'Being struck by the dangerous proximity of the cesspool to the pump well, I lost no time in communicating the facts to the Committee who ordered an inspection of the well to be made forthwith.' This examination was carried out by Jehosephat York, the surveyor, and revealed beyond all doubt the seepage of faecal matter through the decayed brickwork of the cesspool to the well which was less than three feet away.[14]

Some time later Whitehead interviewed Dr Rogers, who had attended the young child. Rogers had not kept his case notes, but expressed the view that the cause of death was acute diarrhoea and not cholera, an opinion he subsequently repeated at a meeting of the Epidemiological Society. Never-theless, there is a strong probability that Whitehead had succeeded in discovering the primary source of the terrible outbreak.

John Snow the doctor, and Henry Whitehead the curate, submitted their reports separately. The committee noted[15] that

'It was Dr Snow who first endeavoured to trace out a relation . . . he supposed might exist between the use of this well-water and the cholera outbreak. The result of his laborious inquiry was in favour of that supposition. Mr Whitehead entertaining, at first, adverse views ended his special investigation of Broad Street by a remarkable confirmation of Dr Snow's numerical results.'

In the light of this imposing body of evidence, and without necessarily accepting Snow's hypothesis regarding the cause of cholera, the committee reached the unanimous conclusion that 'the sudden severe and concentrated outbreak beginning on August 31st and lasting for the few early days in September was in some manner attributable to the use of the impure water of the well in Broad Street'.[16]

On 9 August 1855 Lankester presented the committee's report to the vestry.[17] The minutes record that he spoke 'at considerable length and read a portion as well as stated the general character and contents of the same'. There followed a discussion and 'the question being put, and the number for and against found to be equal, the Chairman gave the Casting Vote in favour thereof'. It was only by this narrow margin that this important document came to be published. It consisted of 175 pages and included the individual reports submitted by Snow, Whitehead and York the surveyor, as well as an account of the work and findings of the committee. Despite a protest by the board of guardians against its publication on the grounds of expense, 500 copies of the report were printed. Some of these were circulated to other parochial bodies, and it was hoped that the cost would be met through sales to interested members of the public. In this the committee were disappointed, and in April 1856[18] the vestry requested the sum of £170 12s. 7d. from the poor rate to cover the cost of the inquiry.

The report of the committee of inquiry and John Snow's book *On Cholera* were reviewed in *The Lancet* together,[19] the one being regarded as complementary to the other. Particular attention was given to 'Mr Whitehead's searching inquiry', which established 'that but for this source of water supply (ie the Broad Street pump), the deaths from cholera instead of amounting to seven hundred cases would not have reached fifty'. The writer concluded: 'The evidence is so elaborate that we must refer the reader to the work itself for the details.'

It would appear that, for a time at least, it was not unusual for Whitehead's name to be linked with that of Snow when reference was made to the Soho epidemic. For example, at a meeting of the Epidemiological Society in June 1855,[20] at which Snow read a paper on cholera, one of the speakers remarked during the ensuing discussion that the cause of the outbreak in Soho 'had been entirely explained by the labours of Dr Snow and the Rev Mr Whitehead, a curate of the district'.

Later, in 1871, J Netten Radcliffe, the first permanent inspector on the staff of the medical department of the Privy Council, writing of the transmission of cholera through polluted water, said:

'This doctrine now fully accepted in medicine, was originally advanced by the late Dr Snow; but to Mr Whitehead unquestionably belongs the honour of having first shown with anything approaching conclusiveness the high degree of probability attaching to it. Only now perhaps can the great public importance of the doctrine be clearly appreciated, and the value of Mr Whitehead's inquiry properly estimated'.[21]

It might perhaps be of interest at this point to inquire into the antecedents of this exceptional young clergyman. The details of his career are to be found in the memorial sketch written shortly after his death by his friend Canon Rawnsley.[22] Henry Whitehead was born on 22 September 1825 in Ramsgate, Kent, at Chatham House, a small public school where his father was master. He was the eighth of ten children, and grew up in the school, becoming in due course a pupil and, later, an assistant master. For 22 years Henry lived in the atmosphere of school with his father, Thomas, in the inseparable roles of parent and teacher. Thomas Whitehead is said to have been 'a disciplinarian of the old type': in school he was 'stern and uncompromising', but outside the classroom he was 'tender and kind'. The curriculum at Chatham House was a liberal one for those days, for, although it was based largely on the classics, it included among other things a weekly lecture on the sciences.

Henry was a promising pupil; from an early age he showed marked ability in English composition, and at 12 years was the top of his class in Latin and mathematics. It may be, therefore, that his later capacity for painstaking inquiry and his accuracy of detail sprang from the demands of his classical and mathematical studies conducted for so long in the scholastic environment of his home.

In 1847, having served for three years on the teaching staff under his father, Henry went up to Lincoln College, Oxford. It was while he was at the university that he made up his mind to enter the Church, and, having obtained his BA in 1850, he left to seek ordination. In those days titles were fewer than applicants, and he considered himself fortunate when he was offered a post as assistant curate at £100 per annum by the Vicar of St Luke's, Soho. In 1851, following his ordination as a deacon, he took up his duties among the residents of the crowded slums of the Berwick Street area. By the time the cholera broke out, three years later, he was a welcome visitor in the homes of his parishioners, a fact which proved of great value to him during the four months of his painstaking inquiry.

Whitehead continued his ministry at St Luke's for two years after the epidemic before he left to seek another curacy. In the years that followed he served in several London parishes, where, apart from his ordinary duties, he took a practical interest in many of the social problems of the day, notably in juvenile delinquency.[23] Then, in 1865, the threat of cholera returned again to this country. Several small outbreaks occurred which gave rise to apprehension and foreboding in the mind of the public.

By that time John Snow was dead, and there were still many sceptics of his theory concerning the transmission of cholera by polluted water. (Writing in 1858, John Simon had referred to Snow's 'peculiar doctrine as to the contagiousness of cholera'.) Whitehead, therefore, considered the moment appropriate to publish his own account of the Soho outbreak, principally to sound a warning of the dangers which might arise through neglect of the lessons that it provided.

In his first article published in *Macmillan's Magazine,*[24] he described his investigation in Broad Street, and gave some interesting sidelights which had not been included in the earlier reports. The following passage is characteristic of his clear prose description:

'. . . limited in its extent, brief in its duration, and continually on the wane from the first moment of its appearance was this great outbreak, the like of which had perhaps never before been seen in this country . . . as soon as it began to subside leaving us time for reflection and discussion, we indulged in speculation regarding its origin; but none of us could advance a satisfactory hypothesis, for the simple reason that its facts seemed to contradict all the then prevalent theories concerning the spread of cholera.'

Want of cleanliness, insanitary conditions and intemperance were examined and rejected. There was satisfaction at the initiation of the inquiry by the vestry of St James, although there were some vestrymen who deprecated this step as being 'detrimental to the reputation of the Parish'. But the majority persisted in the intention to establish the cause if it could be found. In the inquiry

'Every local condition of the infected district, such as elevation of site, nature of soil and sub-soil, surface and ground plan, streets and courts, density and character of population, internal economy of houses, cess-pools, house-drains, and sewage was minutely investigated. But though we found much to lament or condemn in most of these particulars, we could not find in them any satisfactory explanation of the sharp line of demarcation which on every side surrounded what we called the 'cholera area'. [He described how John Snow, suspecting the water in the well, had secured the removal of the pump handle.] But scarcely anyone seriously believed in his theory.'

He mentioned his own adverse reaction to Snow's hypothesis, and then went on to describe the local investigation.

'In the face of these objections the evidence implicating the pump kept on accumulating not only in my hands but also in those of the other members of the committee . . . until at length sufficient evidence was collected to bring the whole committee to the unanimous verdict which they finally recorded.'

He mentioned that

'from St Luke's pulpit on September 8th I congratulated the poor old women who formed a considerable proportion of the congregation upon their remarkable immunity from the pestilence. At that time I had been too busy to meddle with hypotheses and had not even heard of Dr Snow's bill of indictment against the pump. The escape of these women, many of whom, living alone, had no-one to send to the well, was one of those 'eccentricities' which found their best explanation in the pump theory.

One of the strongest facts in connection with this inquiry is that the impurity of the well-water was, in point of time, the very last discovery made by the investigation. We collected the evidence already described, not only in ignorance of the fact of the well having been contaminated, but in the face of positive and seemingly reliable evidence to the contrary. The sides of the well had been examined and declared in a report made by order of the Paving Board on November 24th, 1854, 'to be free from any fissures or other communication with drains or sewers by which such matters could possibly be conveyed into the waters'. Both chemical and miscroscopical analyses had 'failed to detect anything which could be pronounced peculiar to the cholera period or capable of acting as a predisposing co-operating or specific agent in the production of that disease'. We stand exonerated from the imputation of seeking to impugn the well-water on the ground of any previous knowledge of its impurity. Indeed for my own part I had a leaning the other way.'

After giving a description of the well as revealed by the surveyor's inspection, he went on to call for an end of the surface wells in London. 'Yet strange to say they are held in great repute.'

He gave details of the circumstances of the fatal cases in No 40 Broad Street, and remarked, 'There was some discussion among the doctors on whether the child did actually have cholera, its own doctor claiming that it did not. The circumstantial evidence is, however, very strong that it was in this way that the epidemic was caused.' Referring to the report to the vestry, he said, 'If it could have been widely circulated it would have rendered it wholly unnecessary for me to write another line on the matter to which it relates.'

Several months later he published a second article in the same magazine[25] entitled 'The influence of impure water on the spread of cholera'. In this he drew attention to the continuing prevalence of cesspools and to the widespread use of shallow wells. He mentioned how difficult it was to convince people of the dangerous condition of such waters when their taste and appearance continued to be satisfactory. Once again he gave the salient details of the Soho epidemic and the manner of its causation. He expressed the hope that what he had written would 'moderate some of the terrifying notions which prevail concerning the causes of cholera'.

Rawnsley[26] tells us that the publication of these articles by Whitehead led to the offer of a post by the editor of the *Daily News*, who is said to have remarked, 'Is there no small bishopric for such a man?' The offer was, of course, not accepted.

Two weeks after the appearance of the second article in July 1866, the disaster of which Whitehead had given forewarning occurred. Cholera broke out in the crowded slums of East London and spread through the very circumstances that he had feared. It was the contaminated water of the River Lee, supplied untreated by the East London Water

Company, which carried the disease into thousands of homes in the localities around the docks.

The Bishop of London called for volunteers to help in the stricken area, from among the clergy who had had previous experience of cholera. Whitehead immediately offered his services, but his vicar objected on the grounds of the risk to the curate's wife and her newly born child. Whitehead insisted that his knowledge and experience were needed, whereat the vicar required him to provide a substitute out of his own slender stipend and also forbade him to return to his home so long as the epidemic lasted. Whitehead submitted to these conditions and went to the aid of the rector of Bethnal Green in the heart of the epidemic area. In the course of his work there he met Netten Radcliffe, who had been sent by Dr Simon to investigate the circumstances of the outbreak. The two men became good friends, and Whitehead gave Radcliffe considerable help in his inquiries which led to the tracking down of the outbreak to its source. In his report[27] Radcliffe made a handsome acknowledgement for this assistance:

> 'In carrying out this investigation concerning the earliest cases I had the good fortune to be assisted by the Rev H Whitehead, MA, to whom Medicine is in a great measure indebted for that elaborate investigation of the cholera outbreak in the parish of St James, Westminster (the Broad Street pump outbreak) which it is now known gives Dr Snow's opinion of its origin a probability practically amounting to a demonstration.'

When on a later occasion Radcliffe publicly acknowledged his indebtedness to Whitehead, the latter modestly discounted the value of his contribution, saying:[28]

> 'He has been good enough to say that I rendered him some assistance on this occasion, but the only assistance he needed was of a kind very easily given, namely, the support of my arm whilst he limped about the banks of the Lee still suffering from the effects of rheumatic fever. . . . I have only to add respecting this epidemic that Mr Radcliffe's inquiry into its causes resulted in further

confirmation of Dr Snow's doctrine on the mode of propagation of cholera.'

With the decline of the East London outbreak, Whitehead returned to his duties in Highgate. In May 1867 he read a paper[29] entitled 'Remarks on the outbreak of cholera in Broad Street, Golden Square, London, in 1854' to the Epidemiological Society of London, of which Radcliffe was then the honorary secretary. This paper is of interest in that Whitehead set out to scotch a rumour that has in fact persisted down to the present day. This was that the closure of the Broad Street pump at John Snow's instigation was responsible for bringing the cholera epidemic to an end. Snow himself never made such a claim, nor had any of the formal inquiries made any comment on the consequences of the removal of the pump-handle. It is possible that this idea originated locally, following the publication of the vestry's report incriminating the pump. But it is Benjamin Ward Richardson who was largely responsible for giving a seemingly authoritative support to this myth. Four years after the Broad Street episode, John Snow died suddenly, and Richardson wrote a memoir of his late friend in which he gave his own version of Snow's intervention at the board of guardians on the night of 7 September 1854:[30]

'When the Vestry men were in solemn deliberation they were called to consider a new suggestion. A stranger had asked in a modest speech, for a brief hearing. Dr Snow, the stranger, was admitted, and in a few words explained his view of the 'head and front of the offending'. He had fixed his attention on the Broad Street pump as the source and centre of the calamity. He advised the removal of the pump handle as the grand prescription. The Vestry was incredulous but had the good sense to carry out the advice. The pump handle was removed and *the plague was stayed*. There arose, hereupon, much discussion among the learned ... but it matters little for the *plague was stayed*.'

In this way the story was sent on its way to a wider audience. It received further reinforcement in 1866, from the pen of Edwin Lankester, who in that year published his version of the Soho epidemic.[31] In referring to the incident of the pump handle he remarked:

'The Board of Guardians met to consult as to what ought to be done. Of that meeting the late Dr Snow demanded an audience. He was admitted and gave it as his opinion that the pump in Broad Street, and that pump alone, was the cause of all the pestilence. He was not believed – not a member of his own profession, not an individual in the parish believed that Snow was right. But the pump was closed nevertheless and *the plague was stayed.*'

Whitehead, who knew the details of the outbreak better than anyone living, was at pains to show that there were no grounds for making such a claim. He began:

'It is commonly supposed and sometimes asserted even at meetings of Medical Societies that the Broad Street outbreak of cholera in 1854 was arrested in mid-career by the closing of the pump in that street. That this is a mistake is sufficiently shown by the following table which, though incomplete, proves that the outbreak had already reached its climax, and had been steadily on the decline for several days before the pump-handle was removed.'

The table revealed the daily toll of the epidemic and showed how the number of fatal attacks had diminished from 142 on 1 September to 14 on 8 September, the day on which the pump was closed. Thereafter it fell to single figures and slowly dwindled away. This table included only residents, and excluded the non-resident work-people who had contracted cholera in the first days and died outside the district. Whitehead added:

'The table, if more complete, would have indicated more clearly even than it does now, the exceeding virulence of the outbreak during its two or three earlier days, and the rapidity of its decline after the climax was passed; and the column of fatal attacks, incomplete as it is, establishes the fact that the climax was reached within a very few hours of the first manifestation of the outbreak. Clearly the original cause of the explosion must very soon have lost much of its fatal power.'

85

This rebuttal of the rumour did not succeed in its purpose. The story of the pump handle, like that of King Alfred and the cakes, was one which caught the popular imagination and was not to be disposed of lightly.

In 1955 the centenary of the publication of John Snow's book *On Cholera* was commemorated by the Epidemiological Section of the Royal Society of Medicine – the direct successor of the Epidemiological Society of London. Professor Bradford Hill, the president of the section, in his address on that occasion, discussed the question of the pump handle yet again, and repeated the substance of the remarks made by Whitehead many years before:[32]

> 'Though conceivably there might have been a second peak in the curve, and though almost certainly some more deaths would have occurred if the pump-handle had remained *in situ*, it is clear that the end of the epidemic was not dramatically determined by its removal. The deaths had already been declining from a marked peak for at least five days.'

He added that Snow recognized this and had 'never occupied the flimsy pedestal upon which some would place him'.

This does not in any way detract from the value of Snow's researches, nor does it throw doubt on his conclusions, which are based on more substantial, though less dramatic, evidence than that afforded by the removal of the handle from the Broad Street pump.

But, to return to 1867, Whitehead, in his address, revealed one important result of the closure of the pump which had not previously been suspected, and which seems subsequently to have been overlooked. He said:

> 'I must not omit to mention that if the removal of the pump-handle had nothing to do with checking the outbreak which had already run its course, it had probably everything to do with preventing a new outbreak, for the father of the infant, who slept in the same kitchen, was attacked with cholera on the very day (September 8th) on which the pump-handle was removed. There can be no

doubt that his discharges found their way into the cess-pool and thence to the well. But, thanks to Dr Snow, the handle was then gone.'

Whitehead pointed out that the evidence indicated that the water from the well was not injurious before 30 August, nor for long after 2 September. It was not to be wondered that the well purified itself, since i) the pollution caused by the infant's discharges ceased on 30 August, ii) the body of water held in the well was not great, and iii) consumption of water was exceptionally high during the early days of the outbreak – some cholera patients drank as much as 17 pints in a day. Concluding, Whitehead remarked:

'The slackened rate of decline after September 3rd. does not, in the present state of knowledge upon the mode of propagation of cholera, need any explanation. I now only wonder that with such a start from the agency of the pump, and with so much material thus supplied for the continuance of the outbreak by other means of communication it had so little power to sustain itself for any length of time after its original promoter had begun to suspend its fatal operation.'

This paper, presented by a parish clergyman to an audience of epidemiologists, is interesting not only for its content but also for the lucid presentation of the data and for the cautious manner in which the conclusions were drawn. It was sub-sequently published in the *Transactions* of the Society.

Whitehead's experiences in the East End of London had aroused his interest and concern for the manifold problems of the residents of this area, and, as a result, in the year following the epidemic, he took up a curacy in Stepney. His two years there were followed by a short spell of service in Hammersmith, after which he returned to dockland as the vicar of St John's, Limehouse. Writing of Whitehead's ministry among the people of this neglected area, Rawnsley[33] says that he was 'working not only as their parish priest, but as the high priest of sanitation and order'. At the end of three years of unremitting toil among the dockworkers at a time of economic slump, he was offered the benefice of Brampton, a small town in Cumberland by the patron, the Earl of Carlisle, and after much deliberation he decided to accept.

In the course of the 23 years which he had served first as assistant curate and later as vicar in seven districts of London, Whitehead had built up a wide circle of acquaintances in many walks of life. Before he left the busy streets of the East End to start a new life as vicar of a quiet country town, these friends combined to present him with a loving cup as a parting gift. The presentation was made at a dinner held in the Rainbow tavern in Fleet Street on 16 January 1874. This occasion was rendered noteworthy in that Whitehead delivered what is said to have been the longest after-dinner speech on record. Many years later a writer in *The Times* gave the following account of the event:[34]

> 'It is a remarkable instance of the way in which character, without any adventitious aids, can impress men, that on the eve of his leaving London, he was entertained at dinner by a body of men, many of them distinguished in their various callings and all of them attracted by the mere personality of the man. It is a proof of his originality and humour that in returning thanks for the toast of his health he was able to fix the attention and sustain the interest of his hearers for three hours on 'Twenty years as a London curate' – probably the longest after-dinner speech on record. Few survivors of the gathering will ever forget the sustained fascination of that speech.'

In the course of this address,[35] Whitehead referred to the two cholera outbreaks with which he had been concerned. He gave the following personal reminiscence of John Snow, probably the only one we have from a source other than BW Richardson's memoir:

> 'Yet for wholly exceptional reasons, I may say a few words about Dr John Snow – as great a benefactor in my opinion to the human race as has appeared in the present century. Dr Snow had long believed that he had discovered the mode in which cholera is propagated and fortunately he was at hand to direct an inquiry into the cause of the Broad Street outbreak, which inquiry resulted

in a remarkable confirmation of his hypothesis. The story of his researches and of this investigation in particular I have elsewhere related at some length and therefore I will not now go into the subject. What I chiefly wish to dwell upon is the calm prophetic way in which he would talk of the ultimate results of the doctrine which he laid down.

"You and I", he would say to me, "may not live to see the day, and my name may be forgotten when it comes, but the time will arrive when great outbreaks of cholera will be things of the past; and it is the knowledge of the way in which the disease is propagated which will cause them to disappear".

He died in 1858 and since his death we have seen a complete revolution in the mode of investigating the causes of cholera and typhoid, a revolution already fruitful in beneficial consequences and destined hereafter to achieve all the important results that he anticipated. He did not in his lifetime receive all the recognition which was due to his genius, though unstinted respect was paid to his character.

"Dr Snow's views on cholera", said a medical friend to me in 1855, "are generally regarded in the profession as very unsound." "If that be the case', I replied, "heresy may be as good a thing in your profession as some of you are apt to suppose in mine."

A portrait of Dr Snow hangs on my study wall and ever serves to remind me that in any profession the highest order of work is achieved not by fussy demand for "something to be done" but by patient study of the eternal laws'.

It is of interest to note that the comment on John Snow's character is one which was generally made and appears on his tombstone.[36] Whitehead's remarkable speech to his friends was taken down verbatim by a shorthand writer and was published later under the title of *Experience of a London Curate*.

In March 1874 he began his ministry in Cumberland and remained there for the rest of his life. So far as is known he never again concerned himself with cholera – the Cumberland fells were far removed from the unhealthy slums of Soho and dockland. As vicar, Whitehead played a leading part in local affairs, particularly in regard to the schools, clubs and friendly societies of the town. It was typical of the man that when on one occasion he was in dispute with the education department about school accommodation in Brampton, he made a personal census of the children of school age in the area, and showed the inaccuracy of the 'estimate' made by the officials of the department.[37]

In later life he became interested in historical and archaeological subjects, and he wrote a number of articles on the registers, the bells and the plate of the churches in the diocese of Carlisle. These display the same keen sense of observation and concern for accuracy of detail which were so marked in his cholera studies.

On 5 March 1896, at the age of 70, he died suddenly at Lanercost Priory, and was buried in the churchyard at Brampton. He left a widow and two unmarried daughters.

The memory of Henry Whitehead is kept to this day in Brampton. In 1956, the sixtieth anniversary of his death was marked by a public lecture given by the present incumbent, the Rev K Harper, in which he touched upon many aspects of the life of this singular parson.[38] In the same year, too, the headstone on Whitehead's grave which had fallen into disrepair was restored by the local congregation.

Henry Whitehead is remembered as a devoted pastor and as an enlightened worker for social improvement. But his endeavours in the epidemiological field were by no means negligible. The value of his work on cholera in no way detracts from that of John Snow, rather it is complementary to it. To Snow undoubtedly belongs the credit for having first elucidated the means whereby cholera is spread. In his lifetime his discovery was received with incredulity by the majority of the medical profession who were satisfied that the transmission of this and other epidemic diseases could be explained in terms of miasmata. Whitehead, entering into this controversy almost by chance, had no reason to doubt the truth of the prevailing doctrine. Snow's indictment of the Broad Street pump seemed at the outset as unsatisfactory to him as it did to the medical inspectors of the board of health. It is, therefore, greatly to his credit that when the opportunity presented itself, he was not content to leave the issue undetermined. For him it was not sufficient to seek to refute Snow's explanation by argument, but by demonstration. This he set out to do, and, in the event, his research constituted a remarkable confirmation of the hypothesis he had anticipated that it would refute. His discovery of the manner in which the well had become contaminated provided the final link in the chain of evidence which put the issue beyond reasonable doubt. It should not be forgotten that, but for Whitehead's work, Snow's explanation of the Soho epidemic would have remained presumptive.

Although without special training or knowledge in medical matters, Whitehead displayed the keen observation, the strict regard for objectivity and measurement and the ability to evaluate evidence which are the hallmarks of sound scientific inquiry. His studies, together with those of John Snow, provide an outstanding example of the fruitful combination of the intelligent layman and the medical specialist.

Whitehead's work served both to confirm and underline the thesis that cholera is a water-borne disease, which, with his persistent efforts to bring this knowledge into practical use, made a signal contribution to the advancement of public health.

ACKNOWLEDGEMENTS

My thanks are due to Professor JM Mackintosh and Professor WS Walton for their encouragement and advice, to the Archivists of the London County Council and the City of Westminster for their valuable assistance, and to Miss J Cooper for her help in preparing the paper for publication.

REFERENCES

1 Snow J. On the mode of communication of cholera (2nd edition). London, 1855, pp 38–40.
2 The Times, London, 15 September 1854, p 9.

3 Whitehead H. The cholera in Berwick Street. London, 1854.

4 General Board of Health. Report of the committee for scientific inquiries in relation to the cholera epidemic of 1854 (appendix). London, 1855, p 158.

5 *Ibid*, p 52.

6 General Board of Health. Report of the Medical Council to the Rt Hon Sir Benjamin Hall in relation to the cholera epidemic of 1854. London, 1855, p 7.

7 Vestry of St James's Westminster. Minutes, 2 November 1854. (MSS, Westminster City Archives.)

8 *Ibid*, 23 November 1854.

9 *Ibid*, 14 December 1854.

10 Vestry of St James's Westminster. Report on the cholera outbreak by the Cholera Inquiry Committee. London, 1855, p v.

11 *Ibid*.

12 *Ibid*, Mr Whitehead's report, pp 121–69.

13 *Ibid*, p 159.

14 *Ibid*, Mr York's report, pp 170–4.

15 *Ibid*, p 76.

16 *Ibid*, p 83.

17 Vestry of St James's Westminster. Minutes, 9 August 1855.

18 Board of Guardians of St James's Westminster. Minutes, 4 April 1866. London County Archives.

19 Lancet. London, 1855, II, 524.

20 Lancet. London, 1855, II, 11.

21 Rawnsley HD. Henry Whitehead – a memorial sketch. Glasgow, 1898, p 40.

22 *Ibid*, pp 1–48.

23 Whitehead H. The Times, London, 26 December 1855, p 9.

24 Whitehead H. The Broad Street pump: an episode in the cholera epidemic of 1854. Macmillan's Magazine, Cambridge, December 1865, p 113.

25 Whitehead H. The influence of impure water on the spread of cholera. Macmillan's Magazine, Cambridge, July 1866, p 182.

26 Rawnsley HD, *vide supra*, p 41.

27 Privy Council. Ninth report of the medical officer, for 1866. (Appendix No 7.) Report by Mr J Netten Radcliffe on cholera in London and especially the eastern districts, p 288.

28 Whitehead H. Experience of a London curate. Clapham, 1874.

29 Whitehead H. Remarks on the cholera outbreak in Broad Street, Golden Square, London, in 1854. Trans. Epid. Soc. of London, 1867, III, 99–105.

30 Snow J. On chloroform and other anaesthetics – with a memoir of the author by Benjamin W Richardson. London, 1858.

31 Lankester E. Cholera, what it is and how to prevent it. London, 1866, p 34.

32 Hill A Bradford. Snow – an appreciation. Proc. Roy. Soc. Med., 1956. XLVIII, 1010.

33 Rawnsley HD, *vide supra*, 1898, p 82.

34 The Times, 9 March 1896, p 6.

35 Whitehead H. Experience of a London curate. Clapham, 1874.

36 Chave SPW. John Snow and cholera in London. London School of Hygiene, 1955, p 84.

37 Rawnsley HD, *vide supra*, 1898, p 114.

38 Harper Rev K. Personal communication, 1956.

5

A thousand new men

In the life of nations there are moments when the people are ready for the next great leap forward, old institutions are reformed and new ones created, interspersed with long periods of quieter consolidation. The five years following the passing of the great Reform Bill in 1832 was a period of major advance, as were the five years following the general election of 1945 which saw the founding of the welfare state and the creation of the National Health Service. The five years which followed the general election of 1868 was yet another such period. Gladstone's Liberal government took office and then carried through a massive programme of social reform.

There was reform of the civil service with the opening up of all posts in the government service to all applicants through public examinations. The army ended the sale of commissions. The creation of the High Court of Justice reformed the administration of justice. Trade unions were accorded legal recognition; religious tests for admission to the universities were abolished; and secret ballots were introduced in parliamentary elections. The great leap forward came with Foster's Education Act of 1870 which provided for universal elementary education.

It was in the context of this ferment that there came the next major advance in the organisation of public health and in the career of its principal agent, the medical officer of health. The decade which followed the setting up of the medical department at the Privy Council, under Dr John Simon, has sometimes been called the 'sanitary doldrums', a period in which nothing very much seemed to happen. And at first glance this would seem to be true. However, if we examine the statute book we find that year by year Parliament had been passing acts having some sanitary relevance but mainly of only limited and local application. The administration of these acts was a complete mess. They had created a multitude of local bodies including boards of guardians, town councils, boards of health, commissions of sewerage, highways commissions, improvement commissions, select vestries and others all dabbling in the field of public health and asserting their right to do so.

By 1869 there were only five full-time appointments of medical officers of health outside the metropolitan area. They were at Southampton (with an annual salary of £200), Birkenhead (£350), Leeds (£500), Manchester (£500), and, of course, Liverpool (£1,000). Most towns looked on the MOH as an expensive luxury they could afford to do without. Some towns had made an appointment, then, finding that the MOH wanted to spend money, got rid of him as quickly and quietly as they could. In all, only about 85 authorities outside London were employing even the part-time services of an MOH.

While English society at that time continued to pay lip service to the principles of laissez-faire – the sanctity of individual rights and private property and the deeply-rooted independence of local government from central control – there was by now developing a realisation that there were national problems which required solutions at the national level. The time was ripe for change.

The spark came from the inspiration of Henry Rumsey (1809–76), a surgeon and a staunch proponent of a system of state medicine which he had put forward in his book *Essays on State Medicine* published in 1856. On his initiative the British Medical Association and the Social Science Association sent a memorial to Disraeli, the then Prime Minister, urging him to set up a royal commission to review the whole sanitary scene. Disraeli, who had a high regard for public health – he had coined the catch-phrase *'sanitas sanitatum omnia sanitas'* – agreed, and in 1868 announced his intention to set up such a commission. However, he had, perhaps unwisely for himself, extended the franchise to the urban working class in the second Reform Act of 1867, and in the ensuing election he was, as he put it, 'dished by the Whigs'. Gladstone took office and immediately implemented Disraeli's intention by appointing the Royal Sanitary Commission.

The commission reported two years later and made recommendations which led to the 1871 Local Government Act and the 1872 and 1875 Public Health Acts. The 1872 act initially created 1,453 urban and rural authorities, although the numbers were to change over time. In the urban districts, the town councils of the municipal boroughs became the sanitary authorities; in the non-municipal towns the local boards of health took these powers; in the rural districts the boards of guardians assumed these responsibilities. All had to appoint a medical officer of health. They were allowed to combine together for this purpose and many of them did so. They were also required to appoint a nuisance inspector.

Thus it was that more than a thousand new posts suddenly came into being. The act did not require that they should be full-time, nor did it debar the holders from private practice. In the majority of cases the response of the local sanitary authorities was to make a token compliance with the act by the appointment of a general practitioner on a part-time basis – what came to be called a 'ten pound a year man'. In some rural areas the boards of guardians appointed Poor Law medical officers as part-time medical officers of health, but after 1880 the Local Government Board discouraged this practice. For many years the full-time medical officer of health remained a relatively rare phenomenon. Indeed, by the end of the century the number of men who were holding full-time appointments did not exceed 100. These were either working in the large towns or cities or in the combined rural districts where the size of the task made such an appointment essential.

The central department offered bait of a grant of half the salary of the MOH on condition that it could prescribe the terms of his appointment. The number of local authorities who accepted the grant on these terms cannot now be ascertained, but of the 44 towns with populations exceeding 35,000, 36 rejected the offer and its implied control. Of such stuff was the spirit of local independence made.

During the 20 years in which Simon had been medical officer in succession to the General Board of Health, the Privy Council and then to the Local Government Board he had worked single-mindedly towards the establishment of a properly organised system of public health for the nation – and within that system he had envisaged an essential role for the medical officer of health. He was largely instrumental in securing the appointment of medical officers right across the country. If it was Chadwick who brought the MOH into being it was Simon who made him a national institution. Then, through the great Public Health Act of 1875, of which he was the author, he provided the MOH with a charter of action and armed him with the powers through which he was able to operate with greater effect for the next 60 years.

Another noteworthy innovation made by Simon was the practice of publishing his annual report to his chief. He began this in 1856 and continued until the end of his career. Once begun the practice was taken up and continued by his successors in office, of whom there have been 12 to the present time. In 1920, George Newman, the first chief medical officer at the Ministry of Health entitled the report, appropriately, 'On the state of the public health' and it has retained that title ever since. The report is important, for it is to the nation as a whole what the annual report of a local medical officer of health was to his district. It gives an account of the health and health problems of the general population and the development of services to meet those problems. This series of reports gives a continuing assessment of these matters going back to 1856. It is unique in the world and we owe its inception to Simon.

Within a short time of the passing of the act almost half of the large towns had taken steps to appoint a medical officer of health. There was no shortage of applicants for full-time posts; most towns had between 20 and 30 to choose from. Broadly speaking, the men who secured the whole-time appointments came from two sources. There were men like W Trench (Liverpool), J Leigh (Manchester), G Goldie (Leeds) and H Yeld (Sunderland) who had been well-known general practitioners in their districts; and there were those like H Armstrong (Newcastle), J Tatham (Salford), F Vacher (Birkenhead) and G Turner (Portsmouth) who stepped straight from resident posts in fever hospitals and dispensaries into these public health appointments. It would seem that a man known locally was at a great advantage in the selection stakes.

It is worth commenting how young many of these men were. J Spear (South Shields) was only 24. G Turner was 26; and H Armstrong, J Tatham, F Vacher and G Goldie were all only 30. These young men were to shoulder heavy responsibilities in these new and untried posts in the large towns of England.

This was a particularly critical time in the career of the medical officer of health, for there were three important questions at issue which had to be resolved. First, was the MOH to be a specialist, required to show by special quaifications that he possessed special skills? Second, was he to be a whole-time officer in the local government service and hence to cease to rely on private practice to ensure his income? Third, was he to have security of tenure, and so be able to perform his duties without fear of dismissal at the whim of the body which employed him?

These were issues which affected every medical officer of health and were not quickly or easily resolved. They were complicated by the considerable variation between the nature of the public health task in the big cities and the small rural districts, but above all by the determination of local authorities at all levels to employ and control their MOH for themselves, and to resist any attempt by the central department to over-rule them.

Let us consider the specialist issue first because it was to have important and unexpected implications for the future. By the 1870s the medical faculties of the universities had come to regard sanitary science as beyond the scope of the ordinary curriculum. Up to this time sanitary questions had centred almost exclusively around the prevention of epidemic fevers and these were matters on which every student was instructed. But now, sanitary questions were turning more and more on chemical analysis of food, water and sewage, on technical aspects of sanitary engineering and on housing. They were concerned with physics, particularly its bearing on meteorology, and on vital statistics and their interpretation. The universities now began to see the need to treat sanitary science as a specialist subject and to introduce postgraduate training for doctors wishing to take up careers in this new and developing field.

The first of such courses was started in 1871 at Trinity College, Dublin, by William Stokes, regius professor of medicine, who was a friend and supporter of Henry Rumsey. The course comprised instruction in sanitary law, engineering, vital statistics, meteorology, pathology, chemistry and medical jurisprudence. It led to a diploma in state medicine, a term which was used synonymously with public health.

In 1875 Cambridge followed with a diploma in sanitary science. Within a few years courses were being offered at Manchester, Durham, Oxford, Birmingham, Liverpool, Leeds, Sheffield, Bristol and London (see appendix C). The conjoint board of the Royal Colleges of Physicians and Surgeons also began to examine candidates for a diploma in this subject.

At first a variety of titles was used to denote these courses, including hygiene, sanitary science, state medicine and public health, and the qualifications in these subjects included a certificate, a diploma, a licentiate and a bachelor's degree (see appendix D).

The contents of these courses were very similar. They all used as their basic text EA Parkes' *Manual of Practical Hygiene* which was first written for use in the army. This book established itself as the public health officer's *vade mecum*. Along with this there were also George Wilson's *Handbook of Hygiene and Sanitary Science* and Edward Smith's *Manual for Medical Officers of Health*. Each course included practical work in the laboratory and a period of attachment to an MOH in a local public health department. Every candidate for the diploma had to submit a report of a field study, for example, on a group of houses. In time all these courses were consolidated to lead to the diploma in public health – the DPH.

In 1886 the qualifications were put under the supervision of the General Medical Council when it was enacted 'that any registered medical practitioner to whom a diploma in sanitary science, public health or state medicine has (after examination) been granted by competent authorities shall be entitled to have such diploma entered in the Medical Register'. This signified the formal recognition of the new specialty. Once registration was introduced specialists multiplied. In 1886 there were 263; by 1900 there were almost 700 of them. In 1888 Parliament set the seal of statutory approval on the qualifications by inserting a clause in the Local Government Act of that year requiring the medical officers of health of any district having a population of 50,000 to hold the DPH (or its equivalent).

The Royal Sanitary Commission had recommended that the medical officers of the Poor Law should become medical officers of health for their districts. In this way curative and preventive medicine would have been combined in the same hands. This would have brought the 4,000 practitioners who held Poor Law appointments into public health and would undoubtedly have influenced the character of the public health service in the future. However, Gladstone's administration decided otherwise. It was argued that the Poor Law medical officers had no knowledge or experience of public health work and to have made them medical officers of health would have been a great mistake. This was a view which Simon held very strongly. He wrote and spoke in favour of a medical officer of health who should be concerned specifically with prevention and with the administration of sanitary law.

It was the arrival of Simon's MOH which really began the separation between the practitioners of curative medicine and the health officer whose duties were based on the new discipline of sanitary science. This was to be further influenced by the virtual separation of the medical activities of the public health and the Poor Law sections of the local government board. The districts served by the medical officers of health rarely coincided with those of the medical officers of the guardians. There was little or no cooperation between them; often they pursued conflicting policies. The chief object of the guardians was to deter people from seeking medical relief until driven to do so by serious illness or destitution. By contrast, the MOH was engaged exclusively in prevention through measures of environmental sanitation and the control of infectious diseases in which his clinical skills were limited to diagnosis.

It followed that the new specialists in public health and hygiene began to pay less attention to the clinical aspects of medicine and so became alienated from the majority of the practising members of their profession. To help to cater for the new specialty, the British Medical Association set up a public medicine section. In 1878, the *British Medical Journal* commented on the poor attendance at meetings of the section. 'Discussions on such subjects as the construction of infectious diseases hospitals, condemnation of unsound meat and the registration of disease, however interesting they may be to Medical Officers of Health, can scarcely vie for attractiveness to the great body of men with burning questions which were offered for debate in the programmes of other sections.'

It was not this section of the BMA, but the Society of Medical Officers of Health which was to provide the main forum for discussion of the subjects which concerned the medical officers of health. The society began as the Metropolitan Association (see page 52), almost as a club for the first medical officers of health in London. In 1869 the term 'Metropolitan' was dropped from the title in order to allow extra-metropolitan medical officers of health to join as full members. In the same year, a proposal was received from the Social Science Association for the amalgamation of the scientific meetings of the two bodies with a view to their eventual fusion. Had this proposal been adopted the combined associations could never have become the representative body of the medical officers of health. However, the proposal came to nothing. In 1873, the title of the association was changed to the Society of Medical Officers of Health. After 1875, four autonomous regional associations of medical officers of health were established in the Northwest, Yorkshire, Birmingham and the Midlands, and the Northern Counties, and began to contribute to the central councils of the society.

An important step came in 1888 when the society launched its monthly journal *Public Health*. This replaced the annual transactions which had been printed from 1879 and contained many of the papers which had been read at meetings of the society. The new journal aimed

'to be an authoritative scientific periodical, treating of all matters which concern the Public Health and a faithful mirror of the opinions of the most eminent sanitarians of the present day; and to contain, as far as possible, an annual account of every noteworthy advance in Hygiene which has taken place during the year and help in bringing together under one organisation, societies engaged in the work of preventive medicine'.

Thus wrote Winter Blyth, the first editor. Winter Blyth had lost his post as MOH Okehampton in 1879 when the combined district he served was broken up to save money. In the following year he became the MOH of St Marylebone, the third in succession there, and immediately began to play a prominent part in the affairs of the society. He was the author of *The Composition and Analysis of Food*, which became the standard work on the subject. In 1888 the council invited him to become the founding editor of the new journal. In 1901 he was elected president of the society.

In 1891 a Metropolitan branch of the society was formed to take over the local functions of the original associations whose members had borne the heat and burden of the formative years of the representative body of officers of health. The next step in the development of the society came in 1898 when, at the suggestion of Dr Alfred Hill, MOH Birmingham, all the local associations were incorporated into the society and became its provincial branches. At the same time, two further provincial branches were set up in the Home Counties and in the South. In future years the branches became the backbone of the society and contributed considerably to its proceedings. By 1900 the society had about 600 members, including almost all the full-time medical officers of health and several hundred of the part-timers. As the society grew so it gained recognition both as a learned society in the field of preventive medicine and hygiene and also as the representative body of the medical officers of health. Its very success tended further to institutionalise the separation of the practitioners of public health from their colleagues in clinical practice.

The next issue confronting the MOH at this time was whether he was to become a full-time medical officer in the local government service. At the outset the majority of medical officers of health were general practitioners who took on the local appointment for what was little more than a peppercorn fee. The *British Medical Journal* called them 'amateurs, without proper training in sanitary science', who devoted to their public health duties 'only such scraps of time' as they could spare from their private practice. Nevertheless, most of these men took up these posts out of genuine interest in the subject and concern for its problems, and also because there was an element of prestige attached to the holder of an official appointment. As a local man engaged in private practice in his own locality he kept his links with his fellow colleagues in his district. It was in this rather informal way that preventive and curative medicine continued for a time to keep in touch with one another.

However, before long a new generation of medical officers of health arose who had taken their sanitary diplomas soon after qualifying and had little experience of working among practising doctors. Moreover, by reason of the size and nature of the public health task, the trend was always away from minimal and part-time commitment towards a major and, later, full-time engagement in public health.

Security of tenure remained a problem, however. In his preface to the second edition of his *Manual for Medical Officers of Health*, written in 1873, Edward Smith wrote, 'It is to be regretted that an unexpectedly large proportion of appointments to small areas has been made without concurrence of the Local Government Board and that a number of officers are not under the jurisdiction and protection of the Board'. The 'protection' referred to proved in practice to be purely nominal. Although any MOH appointed with the concurrence of the board could not be dismissed without the board's agreement, the board never failed to consent to such a request from a local authority. More often an employing authority wishing to get rid of an MOH whom it regarded as troublesome simply allowed his appointment to lapse at the termination of his formal engagement. In such cases there was nothing the board could have done even if it had wished to do so.

At times the MOH showed he could be as testy with the board as the board was with him. In 1877, having received the annual report of Dr Francis Bond (MOH, Gloucester Union of Sanitary Authorities) the board wrote back to ask what precautions against infectious diseases were being taken in the district. Bond was irritated and replied 'Experience leads me to the belief that in the present state of sanitary matters, to restrict preventive action to what is indubitably contained within the four corners of the Public Health Act, is to do nothing at all'. Edward Seaton, Simon's successor at the board, sent Bond's letter to John Lambert the permanent secretary, remarking that it was both improper and impertinent, and then stating defensively, 'All Medical Officers of Health are not Dr Bonds (God Forbid!) and many most useful notices and cautions are prepared and circulated to Medical Officers of Health which are quite within the terms of the law'. The board took no further action.

In 1888, *Public Health* published a table giving information about 16 medical officers of health who had been literally 'displaced'. It shows that Dr Macaulay of Honiton Borough whose salary was £25 was dismissed because he 'advocated a better water supply'; Dr Alford of Taunton had his salary reduced from £300 to £100 on grounds of economy; Dr Griffiths of Sheffield had his salary of £600 cut by half because he 'looked up nuisances'; and Dr Roberts of Ruthin Urban District, who was paid £25 per year, was 'technically dismissed' in order that part payment of his salary could be claimed from the board; he was not then reappointed. In none of these instances did the board intervene, not even for Dr Britton of Halifax, who lost his post and a salary of £700 after 13 years.

So where could an MOH who felt himself aggrieved turn for help? Not to the local government board. The relationships between the board and the medical officers of health were always of the most tentative and rarely amounted to positive support in difficult situations. In such a case the MOH was left by the board to stand or fall on his own. The only backing he had was the moral support of his colleagues in the Society of Medical Officers of Health. We see then that after 1872 there followed an uphill struggle before the MOH finally emerged as a medical officer in the local government service, holding a statutorily recognised qualification (1926), occupying a full-time post (1929), and secured from arbitrary dismissal by the protection of the minister (1922). And only then was the prescription, written long before by Chadwick, finally fulfilled.

It was said earlier that the Public Health Act of 1872 created more than a thousand posts. How many medical officers of health were there? A parliamentary return published in 1888 showed that in England and Wales there were 269 authorities linked together into 37 combined districts each appointing an MOH. For the rest of the country, outside London, there were 876 urban and 436 rural sanitary authorities, each of which appointed one or more medical officers of health, so that 881 medical officers served the urban and 572 served the rural districts. This made a total of 1,490 medical officers of health outside London. Of these 1,490 medical officers, 1,020 were paid £50 a year or less; only 90 of the total were not allowed to engage in private practice; and only 190 held appointments which were not limited by time.

Thus, at that time, the norm was a part-time medical officer of health earning his living through private practice. However, it was the 90 or so men holding full-time appointments in the large towns, and their colleagues in London, who set the standards and determined the course of public health activity. They were responsible for well over half of the population of the country. Strategically placed in the towns and cities right across the land, they gave the lead to the public health movement locally and nationally. This leadership was manifested especially through their society and its journal.

It was in this way then that in the years following the passing of the Public Health Act of 1872, the medical officer of health came into being in every part of the country. He was recognised as a specialist in the practice of public health and preventive medicine, but by the same token, he was also destined in time to be recognised as a doctor who did not treat patients. In the eyes both of the medical profession and of the public at large a doctor who did not treat patients was not really a proper doctor. Thus, entry to a career in public health brought to the doctor an undoubted loss of esteem. (For two views of the medical officer of health see appendix E.) But the MOH remained unbowed, for it brought something else by way of compensation – a wider horizon. For him, the patient was not the individual but the population. His task was to prevent disease in and promote the health of 'the greatest number'. That was a big enough and a satisfying enough task for any man.

Through the 1870s and for some time afterwards the work of the medical officer of health continued to be focused on the environment. In 1872 the local government board issued a detailed instructional minute setting out the duties of the medical officer of health under 18 headings (see appendix F). These required him to inspect and report on all matters affecting the public health, to enquire into the occurrence of epidemic diseases, and to advise his authority on appropriate measures to deal with them. He had also to keep a record of his activities, to attend meetings of the authority and to submit an annual report to the authority and to the board (see appendix G). But it was the Public Health Act of 1875 which provided the legal framework within which his work was carried out. This had codified the whole corpus of sanitary law into a single statute of 343 sections. These dealt with:

1) a wholesome and sufficient water supply
2) prevention of pollution of water
3) provision of sewerage
4) regulation of streets, highways and new buildings

5) removal of nuisances
6) inspection of food
7) suppression of infectious diseases and provision of fever hospitals
8) sanitary burial
9) regulation of markets, offensive trades and slaughter-houses
10) the making and enforcement of by-laws.

It has been described as the greatest sanitary code ever enacted in any country. The act was to provide the backbone of English public health law for the next 60 years; rarely indeed has a major statute remained effective for so long. This is a testimony to the man, John Simon, who drafted it.

The conceptual basis of the act was the sanitary idea, and its scientific rationale the physico-chemical theories of MJ von Pettenkofer (1818–1901), the great German hygienist. Not yet was public health practice to be influenced by the discoveries of the bacteriologists. Noxious effluvia from cesspools, sewer gas from drains and obvious dirt and filth, rather than germs, were the enemies to be tackled through sensible sanitary action. Thus on the basis of a false hypothesis much public good was to be achieved. This was the period in which the medical officer of health emerged as the medical sanitarian. Invariably he had at his side the inspector of nuisances; if his district was a large one he might have several such inspectors. Although the inspector had started out as an officer of his authority in his own right, by reason of the nature of his work he gradually came under the surveillance and later the supervision of the medical officer of health.

Apart from the continuing problems of drains, water supplies and insanitary nuisances, three other matters were increasingly occupying the attention of the MOH at this time. They were the adulteration and soundness of food, housing, and infectious diseases. From medieval times the adulteration of food had been of concern to government, and Parliament had made many attempts to stamp it out. In the 18th century acts had been passed against the adulteration of coffee, hops and bread. The problem was always one of enforcement, for apart from the local justices, there was no one to do it and the sale of adulterated food and unsound meat continued largely unchecked.

It was the arrival on the scene of the medical officer of health and his inspectors which made it possible to tackle the problem with greater effect. The first attack was on the sale of unsound meat. At that time there was no official control of the slaughtering of animals and no supervision of meat offered for sale. The MOH soon discovered that he could take action against unwholesome practices under the nuisances legislation. Dr Letheby, Simon's successor in the City, initiated the first successful prosecution in London in February 1861 when he charged a local butcher who had five 'rotten sheep' on sale in his shop. The butcher was fined £10, a not inconsiderable sum in those days, and the carcasses were confiscated. Following this success, seizures and convictions became more frequent, especially in London where the trade in diseased, and therefore cheap, meat for the poor was a profitable one. In 1886 Letheby's inspectors seized and destroyed 350,000 pounds of 'bad meat in addition to game, poultry, fish and venison'.

The problem of private slaughtering remained an intractable one. As long as milking cows were housed inside the towns, private slaughtering continued. The Strand district in London was notorious for its multitude of cellar dairies and was at the same time a main centre for the sale of cheap and unwholesome meat. From time to time the inspectors would swoop on these noisome places and seize all the bad meat they could lay their hands on, but it was not long before further consignments arrived, for there was a ready market for it – the poor people of London were only too ready to keep this noxious trade going and resented official interference in it. Over time many local authorities passed by-laws governing the slaughter of animals and the public sale of meat. By 1878 nearly 700 local authorities had taken this step which strengthened the hand of the MOH in dealing with it.

Allied to this was the continuing problem of adulteration of food which was carried on on a massive scale. Flour was adulterated with alum to produce a white loaf; tea was adulterated with prussian blue; pickles with copper salts; children's sweets with lead chromate; chocolate with iron oxide; beer with nux vomica; butter with crude animal fat; and milk with water – often dirty water from the cattle butt or the farmyard pump.

In 1850, *The Lancet* appointed its own sanitary commission to enquire into the adulteration of food. Its findings so impressed public opinion that a parliamentary commission was appointed to examine the problem and, as a result, the Adulteration of Food Act of 1860 was passed into law. This was amended by a further act in 1872. The general effect of this legislation was to make it an offence to adulterate food or drugs. However, these acts proved difficult to administer and still left the way open to evasion. In 1875 they were superseded by the Sale of Food and Drugs Act. This third attempt to tackle the problem was more effective. It permitted the employment by local authorities of public analysts, because the detection of adulteration was a physico-chemical matter. It affirmed, in effect, that chemistry had become a basic science of public health. Five years later further legislation made the appointment of public analysts mandatory by local authorities over a certain size. In this way, the public analyst and his laboratory became an adjunct to the growing public health scene, occupying the role of expert adviser to the MOH. In some cases, the medical officer of health took up this post himself for an additional fee. Notable among those who were also experienced chemists was Henry Letheby of the City of London. For many years he carried out routine analyses of the water supplies of London and circulated his findings to his colleagues in the Metropolitan area. Letheby was also the first to associate hard water with a reduced mortality.

Then there was housing. This was a problem which faced the MOH from the beginning of his career and was to be with him to the end. It is hard to find any one of them who during this period does not refer to it in his report. The chronic shortage of housing accommodation in the towns led to overcrowding and all the evils associated with it. Only new building could have abated the problem. In the period we are now considering, charitable trusts such as the Peabody Trust and the Guinness Trust made some contribution to meeting this need by providing blocks of 'buildings', as these flats for the working class were called. The local authorities at this time were powerless to do anything in this regard. Along with overcrowding went lack of adequate sanitary facilities and physical defects.

Parliament made a number of half-hearted attempts to deal with the housing problem with a stream of acts, including the Torrens Acts of 1868 and 1879 which dealt with individual unfit dwellings and the Cross Acts of 1875 and 1879 which covered areas of unfit housing. These enactments strengthened the powers of the local authorities to deal with the problem, but these authorities showed themselves unwilling to use these powers for fear of the expense they might incur. So the problem remained.

The Torrens and Cross Acts were superseded in 1882 by the Artisans Dwellings Act. Then in 1885 came the Royal Commission on the Housing of the Working Classes which led directly to the Housing of the Working Classes Act of 1890. This ranks with the Public Health Act of 1875 as a major consolidating statute. It empowered the local authorities to deal with 'unhealthy areas' by improvement schemes, to order the demolition of unfit dwellings and to build public lodging houses. Medical officers of health were not slow to urge their authorities to use their new powers. Despite this spate of legislation, or perhaps because of its inherent uncertainties, several of the larger towns in the industrial north, advised by their medical officers of health, preferred to operate through private acts.

In tackling the many sanitary problems which confronted them, the medical officers of health met considerable opposition from landlords, factory owners, shopkeepers, stallholders and those plying offensive trades. Many of these would try to use their influence with the local authority to persuade the medical officer of health to hold his hand. The MOH was often accused of being a petty Chadwick – a real term of abuse in those days – and also of harming the good name of the town, a complaint to which local councillors were particularly sensitive.

Infectious diseases made up the third main problem which the MOH had to face at this time. The most common infections that were present in the country during this period, either in endemic or epidemic form, were smallpox, diphtheria, scarlet fever, typhoid, typhus and dysentery. When cholera struck the country in 1831, 1848, 1853 and 1866 it was part of a world pandemic and in the intervening periods the country was almost entirely free of the disease. Apart from cholera all the other diseases mentioned were endemic and caused a high mortality which was to continue until the end of the century.

The need to isolate cases suffering from these conditions led to demands for proper hospital accommodation. Standards of provision varied considerably from one district to another. In many places the sole provision was a ward in the workhouse infirmary which only paupers were allowed, or indeed were willing, to enter. In Newcastle, Dr Armstrong was fortunate in having an old established voluntary hospital which he had persuaded his council to take over. By contrast, Dr Spear in nearby South Shields for many years struggled to make do with what he pathetically described as 'the hut on the sands'. As the years went by town after town used the powers conferred under the Public Health Act of 1875 to provide its own fever hospital which came under the charge of the medical officer of health. These institutions were not popular with the general public. The risk of cross-infection was known to be high – a patient would go in with one condition and then would contract another because the cause and mode of transmission of these diseases were not yet understood. Furthermore, paupers and non-paupers were admitted on the same terms. This element of social equality lowered the esteem of these hospitals and this attitude was to persist for many years.

Under the administrative arrangements which obtained at that time the medical officer of health did not become aware of the existence of infectious disease in his district until he received a notification of death, so that by then the outbreak was often widespread. Starting in 1881 the society began to press for the compulsory notification of specified infectious diseases. At first, the general practitioners objected to this proposal on the grounds that it constituted an interference in their practice. The president of the local government board was also apprehensive lest this should lead to an increased demand for admission to hospital which would cost money. However, some local authorities, acting on the advice of their medical officers of health, introduced a system of voluntary notification in which a fee was paid to general practitioners for providing this information. By 1882, 18 large towns were operating such a scheme.

The society continued to press the board to introduce general legislation and, at length, in 1889, the Infectious Diseases Notification Act was passed, permitting any local authority which thought fit to require practitioners to notify the medical officer of health of cases of specified infectious diseases. The diseases which could be required to be notified were cholera, smallpox, typhus, scarlatina, enteric fever, relapsing fever, puerperal fever, diphtheria and erysipelas. This first Notification Act marked an important advance but, being permissive, its implementation was piecemeal, depending on the whim of local authorities, not all of which were prepared to accept the advice of the MOH. The society, with Dr Arthur Newsholme (MOH Brighton) as its principal advocate, continued to press for further legislation, but it took ten years before the Extension Act of 1899 was passed, which made notification of specified infectious diseases to the medical officers of health compulsory throughout the land.

A further development in the system of English local government which affected the medical officer of health came in 1888, when Parliament created two new types of locally elected authorities, county councils and county borough councils. The county councils covered the areas of the old counties and the county boroughs were created from the large towns. The county borough councils became sanitary authorities and were required to appoint medical officers of health. The county councils could do so if they wished, but they were not sanitary authorities as these responsibilities continued to be exercised by the district councils situated within the county borders. At that time the functions of the county medical officer were almost entirely advisory. The medical officers of health of the local sanitary authorities were required to submit their annual reports to him and he was empowered to recommend any actions that he considered would enable them to fulfil their statutory duties more effectively. In 1909 the appointment of county medical officers was made compulsory and in the years that followed their responsibilities were considerably expanded. In 1902, the county medical officers combined together to form the Association of County Medical Officers of Health. This association ran in parallel with the society but never merged with it because of the need to maintain an independent relationship with the County Councils Association and other bodies.

Another significant development in this period was the creation by the local government board of port sanitary authorities under powers conferred by the Public Health Act of 1875. By this time the old system of quarantine was falling into disfavour, not least because it was ineffective and also because it brought about a considerable interference with trade. Gradually, the new port sanitary authorities substituted for quarantine a system of medical inspection of crews and passengers of ships at the point of entry to home waters or into port. Under this system a ship was detained only long enough for this inspection to be made, for any sick patients to be dealt with, possibly by removal to an isolation hospital, and for such measures of disinfection as were required to be carried out.

Each port sanitary authority (later to be known as a port health authority) was made up of representatives of the local authority in which the port was situated and of others which abutted on to it. The medical officer of health of the principal district involved generally became the port medical officer. His duties in this new office were, in principle, similar to those which he carried out in his district. In addition, he became superintendent of the isolation hospital to which patients believed to be suffering from infectious diseases were taken on removal from ship.

A port medical officer had one or more assistant medical

113

officers and port sanitary inspectors who, with him, made up the public health establishment of the port. The medical officers boarded every ship entering port which had any sickness on board and took appropriate action. The inspectors were responsible for the disinfection of ships, for general sanitary work around the port and for the inspection of imported food. After the discovery of the link between rats, fleas and plague, the inspectors also became responsible for rodent control on ships and in the docks.

The Public Health Act of 1875 marked the peak of environmental sanitation as a notionally complete system of health for the nation and it continued under its own momentum for many years. However, towards the end of the century the sanitary idea began to be overtaken by a new idea, a new concept, the concept of the individual and his, or her, personal health needs.

The great feats of sanitary engineering pioneered by medical officers of health had been accompanied by substantial improvements in the public health. The general death rate had fallen from 25 to 15 per thousand persons since the publication of Chadwick's report, and the expectation of life of a male at birth had increased from 40 years in 1840 to 50 years in 1900 – a marked massive improvement in health, adding years of life to the average person. Nevertheless, despite all this, the MOH had no grounds for complacency, because the infant mortality rate, perhaps our most sensitive index of social health, remained obstinately high at about 150 per thousand live births and each year about 4,000 women were dying in childbirth.

It was becoming clear that environmental sanitation was not enough to secure an adequate standard of health for the great mass of the people and that what was needed were services directed specifically towards the needs of vulnerable groups, and the first of these were mothers and children. This swing of interest in the public health movement away from its traditional concern for the environment and towards a new concern for personal health coincided with the turn of the century. It was to put a new face on public health and to transform the work of the medical officer of health.

6

The rise and fall of the
medical officer of health*

Sydney Arthur Monckton Copeman was born in 1862 and
died in 1947. For the greater part of his professional life he
was engaged as an investigator and administrator in the field
of public health. It is appropriate, therefore, that this lecture
in his honour should be concerned with one aspect, an
important aspect I suggest, of the public health movement
in this country. Moreover, it is highly probable that Dr
Monckton Copeman was himself an observer of many of the
events that I shall be describing.

I discovered that among the many offices he held was
that of chairman of the board of studies in hygiene of the
University of London. Now it happens that I was myself for
several years the academic secretary to that same board, so
that I can claim a link, if only a slight and tenuous one, with
him, and I am very happy to do so.

And now to our purpose . . .

On the night of Sunday 31 March 1974 an event of no
small significance in the social history of medicine in this
country took place. For it was on that night that the medical
officer of health, the local health officer whom we had had in
this country for a century and a quarter, passed into the
pages of the history book. This is not the moment, I believe,
to make a final appraisal of his contribution to the public weal
– we are still too close to the event for that. What I hope to do
here, therefore, is to sketch out his curriculum vitae, touch

---

* The Monckton Copeman Lecture, delivered to the Faculty of the
History of Medicine and Pharmacy of the Worshipful Society of
Apothecaries on 5 February 1979 and reprinted from *Community
Medicine* (1980) 2:36–45. Inevitably there is overlap in the material of this
chapter and that of chapters 1, 2 and 5. To avoid too much repetition the
editors have omitted some paragraphs of the original lecture. These
omissions are indicated by * * *.

on some of the significant events in his career, look at some of the problems he faced and some of the things he attempted to do, in the course of his lifespan of 127 years until, at length, he reached that fateful night in 1974.

As I have said, the moment of his passing can be fixed with certainty; so too his beginning can also be stated with fairly reasonable confidence. It was in the early months of 1842, his progenitor being that formidable genius Edwin Chadwick.

In his well-known 'Report on the sanitary condition of the labouring population', Chadwick wrote as follows

> 'That for the general promotion of the means necessary to *prevent* disease it would be good economy to appoint a district medical officer, independent of private practice, and with the security of special qualifications with responsibility to initiate sanitary measures and reclaim the execution of the law.'

This was the moment of conception of the medical officer of health.

There had, of course, been a cadre of medical officers in the public service before this time, to wit, the medical officers of the Poor Law, who were employed by the local guardians to provide medical care for the sick poor. But their concern was primarily with *treatment*; the task of the new man was to be essentially with *prevention*.

And, as Chadwick said, it would be good *economy* to have him – economy because, as experience at the Poor Law office had shown, disease meant waste and imposed a heavy burden on the community, not least in the support of those reduced to penury through sickness affecting themselves or their breadwinners. Prevent the one, he said, and you would prevent the other; prevent the disease and you would prevent the waste.

The reason, or rather the principal reason, in Chadwick's mind for bringing the MOH to birth was not humanitarian – no one ever accused Chadwick of having a heart – but economy, because it would make sense in the effective ordering of the public health system, or in the jargon of today, because it promised to be cost-effective.

Chadwick recommended the setting up of local boards of health to be responsible for carrying out sanitary reforms in their areas, each of which should appoint a medical officer as its expert adviser. At the centre there should be a government board which through its inspectorate would exercise oversight over the whole system. Chadwick's proposals were to be implemented, albeit in a watered-down fashion, in the Public Health Act of 1848, but not before two authorities, inspired by his sanitary idea, had anticipated some of its provisions.

It was in Liverpool on 1 January 1847 that the medical officer of health first saw the light of day. Under a private act, the Liverpool Corporation had secured parliamentary sanction for the appointment of an MOH and immediately used its newly won power to bring him to birth in the person of William Henry Duncan [see chapter 1].

Duncan was more important for what he was than for what he did; he was the first man in. Far more important in the long run was to be the appointment of John Simon as the first medical officer of health of the City of London. For Simon was to win for the new office the seal of acceptability which could never have been done by Chadwick, and to give it a stamp of authority that could not be gainsaid. In his new post he set a standard of informed and impartial comment on all matters affecting the public health which won respect and gained attention well beyond the confines of the City.

His reports to the City fathers, couched in the rich, flowing language of the educated Victorian gentleman he was, were published verbatim in columns of *The Times* and read right across the nation. [A sample appears at the end of this chapter.]

As we read his early reports on the City, along with the elegant language, which I admit I enjoy, we find that there is a modern ring about much of his work not least in his recognition of the value of statistics, and indeed, of up-to-date, one might almost say of up-to-the-minute, statistics. For through the cooperation of William Farr [1809–1883] at the General Register Office, Simon was able to arrange that every Tuesday morning the vital statistics of the City for the previous week should be on his desk. From such initiatives were to grow the information systems of our own day.

It is expected of the Monckton Copeman Lecture that it should make reference to the City of London of which Monckton Copeman was himself a Freeman. And certainly, the comment is well worth making that in appointing Simon, the corporation made a signal contribution to the public health, not only of the City, but, in the end of the country as a whole, for in his later years he was to become very much the elder statesman of English public health.

The 1848 Act for Promoting the Public Health, to give it its full title, is by any reckoning an important landmark in our history. But in so far as it was intended to launch the MOH on to a countrywide stage it was largely a failure. For despite the encouragement given by Chadwick very few local authorities thought fit to take advantage of their power to create these posts. Most of them, it seems, regarded the MOH as an expensive luxury they could afford to do without, so that five years later only 35 medical officers are known to have been appointed.

The next real advance came in 1855 with the reform of local government in London. The bill which was to bring this about embodied two important provisions which later were to be applied to the country as a whole. First, the London area was to be divided up into districts each to be responsible for its own sanitary administration – and in London there were to be 48 of them. Secondly, each of these authorities was required to appoint a medical officer of health. This came from Simon, who was now medical officer to the general board of health and whose experience in the City had convinced him that if the task of sanitary reform was to be carried out, it must be led at the local level by a medical man.

* * *

In the light of the undoubted success of the introduction of the medical officer of health to London [see chapter 2], it might have been expected that Parliament would follow this up by enacting similar legislation to cover the rest of the country. But this was not to be, or, at least not for many years.

It is true that a few large towns like Glasgow, Edinburgh, Manchester and Leeds did appoint an MOH, but numerous others such as Newcastle, Nottingham and Sunderland did not bother to do so.

Laissez-faire, local initiative or inertia characterised the prevailing order so that by 1870 only about ninety authorities outside London were employing the services of a medical officer of health.

Then by a wave of the parliamentary wand more than a thousand new posts were suddenly created [as described in the previous chapter]. It happened like this.

When Gladstone took office in 1869 he found sanitary administration in a state of near chaos. There were some 160 acts of Parliament in force containing sanitary provisions but so mixed up that even the lawyers could not unravel them. Gladstone took action by setting up a royal commission to review the whole sanitary scene. In its report, presented two years later, the Royal Sanitary Commission made three important recommendations which were to determine the scope and pattern of the public health system for over 50 years to come.

They were: first, that there should be one central department of government, with responsibility for the public health; secondly, that the whole country should be divided up into districts (like London before this) each of which should be made responsible for sanitary action at the local level; and thirdly, that this mass of sanitary legislation should be consolidated into a single statute.

And so it was that the 1871 Local Government Board Act established the central department, the 1872 Public Health Act created the local sanitary authorities and the 1875 Public Health Act codified the law.

From the point of view of the MOH it was the Public Health Act of 1872 which marked the turning point of his career. For on the representation of Simon, who was now medical officer to the Privy Council, each of the sanitary districts into which England and Wales was divided was *required* to appoint a medical officer of health. And there were 1,400 of them. This literally put the MOH on the map right across the country. Up to that time a local board could employ or dispense with the services of an MOH as it wished. From then onwards, although the authority might dislike, or even dismiss, the *man*, it could not dispense with the *office*.

The act required the appointment of an MOH, it did not require that he should have any special training or qualifications. However, the need to provide training for doctors entering the new specialty was quickly felt and was first met in Ireland. It was in 1871 that Trinity College, Dublin, started a course of postgraduate training leading to a diploma in state medicine, later on to be called a diploma in public health, the DPH. Cambridge followed in 1875 with a diploma in public health and before long almost every university and medical school had followed suit. In 1886 the qualifications were put under the supervision of the General Medical Council and made registerable. Two years later, Parliament set the seal of statutory approval on the qualifications by requiring the MOH of any district having a population of 50,000 to hold the DPH.

This was a good start, but because of the lethargy of the central department the next step was many years away, for it was not until 1926 that an order was made requiring every MOH appointed after that date to hold the DPH, and even here there was an escape clause exempting anyone who had held the post of MOH for three years. It was only in 1936 that this last loophole was closed. Thus, slowly and belatedly, the MOH won his spurs as a specialist, and the DPH became the criterion of proficiency in public health, the hallmark of this specialty in the faculty of medicine.

But in those early days the MOH had other things to worry about apart from his training and qualifications. He was concerned about his salary, his security and his status. In the matter of salary, Liverpool paying £1,000 a year was always in a class by itself; £450 was the more usual figure for a full-time job, with an extra £50 for acting as borough analyst or superintendant of the local fever hospital, which many of them did. Each authority fixed its own salary, there were no annual increments and the amount could be altered at will. Woe betide any man who was too enthusiastic for sanitary reform. The MOH of Fulham, who put forward a comprehensive scheme of sanitary improvement for his district, had his salary cut from £600 to £300 for his pains.

As with salaries, so also with security. The act positively discouraged the making of appointments for more than five years. Indeed, the central department, whenever it had the power to do so, limited appointments to only three years. And, as many of the local authorities, particularly the small ones, were employing medical officers only to comply with the letter of the law, not a few candidates received the quiet intimation that their salary and appointments were safe so long as they made only minimal demands on the rate fund.

Along with security of tenure there was also the question of whole-timeness. Most of the small authorities made part-time appointments, expecting their MOH to earn his keep out of general practice, and paid him as little as £10 a year for his services.

The resolution of all these issues of salary, security and status was complicated by the considerable difference in the nature of the public health task between the big cities on the one hand and the small rural districts on the other, but above all by the determination of local authorities at all levels to employ and control their MOH for themselves, and to resist any move to over-rule them by the central department.

But what was the 'central department' to which I have been referring? It was, of course, the local government board. This had been created by Gladstone, following the Royal Sanitary Commission, by bringing together Public Health and the Poor Law into one department – creating in effect the 19th century equivalent of our Department of Health and Social Security.

This was undoubtedly the biggest setback that English public health ever suffered. For it burdened the infant service with a millstone about its neck that it had to endure for half a century. The arrangement within the department was such that public health was subordinated to the pinch-penny policies of the destitution authority. The board was so busy keeping the ledgers of the Poor Law (and those ledgers were most scrupulously kept) that it seems never to have had

121

the will to look out of the window to see what were the real *health* needs of the nation. Advances there were, important advances, but rarely indeed were they the result of leadership from the centre; instead they came through local initiative and voluntary effort taken up and led by enterprising medical officers of health.

So what were the relationships between the board and the medical officer of health? They were of the most tentative kind, and rarely, if ever, amounted to positive support in difficult situations. In such a case the MOH was left by the board to stand or fall on his own. The only backing he had was the moral support of his colleagues in the Society of Medical Officers of Health. Security for the MOH had to wait until after World War I, when public pressure and political wisdom swept the board away and created the Ministry of Health.

It was only in 1922 that an order was made which laid down that an MOH could not be dismissed without the consent of the Minister. Finally, in 1929, Parliament ruled that all appointments were to be made on a full-time basis.

So we see that after 1872 there followed an uphill struggle lasting 60 years before the MOH finally emerged as a medical officer in the local government service, holding a statutorily recognised qualification, occupying a full-time post and secured from arbitrary dismissal by the protection of the minister. And only then was the prescription written by Chadwick long before, finally fulfilled.

So much then for specialty, security and status. I have dwelt at some length on the issues which confronted the MOH in his early years, for these were formative years, years which determine the character of a man or of an institution. But in between worrying about the terms and conditions of his job, what else was he doing? What about his work?

During the 1870s and for some time after it continued to be focused on the environment and was carried out within the framework of the Public Health Act of 1875. This had codified the sanitary law and provided a charter for action by the MOH. The conceptual basis of the act was the sanitary idea; it was scarcely influenced by the discoveries of the bacteriologists. Noxious effluvia from cesspools, sewer gas from drains and obvious dirt, rather than germs, were the enemies to be tackled through sensible sanitary action. Thus on the basis of a false hypothesis much public good was to be achieved.

But apart from drains and sanitary nuisances, two other problems were increasingly occupying the attention of the MOH at this time; they were infectious diseases and housing. [See chapter 5.]

The need to isolate cases of infectious diseases led to demands for proper hospital accommodation. Standards of provision varied considerably from one town to another. In many towns the sole provision was a ward in the workhouse infirmary, which only paupers were allowed, or indeed for the most part, were willing to enter. As years went by, town after town had to set up its own municipal fever hospital to meet the need for the isolation and proper nursing care of patients suffering from infectious diseases, of which diphtheria and scarlet fever were, after smallpox, the most virulent.

Housing was the other subject which came to be of increasing concern to the MOH. It is hard to find any one of them who does not deal with it in his reports. Hill of Birmingham is worth quoting. He writes, not without a touch of grim humour:

'A very common practice is to erect houses back to back, in some cases this peculiarity of disposition is apparently necessary to prevent them from falling down, or being blown over, so flimsily are they built; but such a mode of construction does prevent something else that matters, namely, a through draught.'

On the same subject, there is a pathetic note in a comment by Russell of Glasgow who describes how he used to go cautiously down the unlighted steps of the tenements 'so as not to stumble over children playing at houses on the stairs'.

Whereas other problems of the environment – water supplies, sewage disposal and so on – were, over the years, to become less acute, the problems of housing in relation to basic physical amenities and to sheer human overcrowding were to remain a continuing commitment of the MOH to the end of his career.

With the passage of time the work of the MOH grew as did the size of his department. Duncan of Liverpool had laboured alone; 40 years later Armstrong of Newcastle headed a team of 20. It included 12 smartly uniformed sanitary inspectors, a chief clerk (who wore a top hat as a sign of his status) as well as other office staff and assistants. I mentioned his fever hospital [chapter 5]. This had a consultant physician, nurses and helpers, all of whom, together with the patients, were firmly ruled over by the matron. (Any resemblance between Matron and Queen Victoria was scarcely accidental!)

The Public Health Act of 1875 marked the high water mark of environmental sanitation as a notionally complete system of health for the nation, and it continued under its own momentum for many years. However, towards the end of the century the sanitary idea began to be overtaken by a new idea, a new concept, the concept of the individual and his or her personal health needs.

*   *   *

If, as historians, we look for beginnings, for starting points in place and time, I think we can fairly locate this one in Salford in Lancashire in 1862. For there, the Salford Ladies Voluntary Sanitary Association, a body of well-meaning middle-class ladies, employed 'a good motherly woman' to visit the homes of the working class to teach the women-folk about the care and nurture of their children. From these small beginnings there was to grow health visiting as a professional service organised within the ambit of the medical officer of health. If the sanitary inspector was always the right-hand man of the MOH, the health visitor was, over time, to become equally close, shall we say, on his left hand.

The year 1902 saw the passing of the Midwives Act which bade fair to end the career of Mrs Gamp, the untrained, unwashed handywoman who performed her lowly function for small fee and small beer, and to replace her with a trained professional midwife, first under the surveillance of the

MOH and later as a member of his staff. Improved care of mothers in childbirth was to contribute to the slow, but steady, decline in maternal mortality which was to take place through the years that followed.

Concern over the fitness of the nation, particularly as a result of the disclosure of the high rejection rate for service in the army in the Boer War, led to the setting up of the Committee on Physical Deterioration in 1904, and so directly to the founding of the school medical service in 1907.

We should note that this service, the first of our personal health services, was *not* put under control of the local government board, for that would have been to stunt its growth from birth. Through the initiative of Robert Morant, the far-sighted permanent secretary of the board of education, a medical department was set up there under Dr (later Sir George) Newman to exercise central control. Morant and Newman devised a simple procedure for linking the new service for schoolchildren with that for the local population in general. They simply encouraged the appointment of the MOH as the principal school medical officer for his area. So from this time onwards, the MOH wore two hats; he was at once medical officer of health for his district responsible to his public health committee, but he was also principal school medical officer and so responsible to the education committee of his authority. This was a happy arrangement that was to last until 1974.

The school medical service introduced a system of routine medical inspection of children at school which brought to light a great mass of hitherto untreated diseases and disorders, the nature and amount of which had scarcely been suspected. For example, in 1910, the medical inspection of six million children revealed:

Unclean heads and bodies: 30–40%   Defective hearing: 3–5%
Serious defect of vision: 10%   Suppurating ears: 1–3%
Enlarged tonsils: 6–8%   Ringworm: 1%
Readily recognisable TB: 1%   Heart disease: 1%
Malnutrition: 'Widespread'

This then was the size of the problem and the school medical service immediately went into action to deal with it.

Hungry children were fed with a bowl of soup and a hunk of bread. Dirty children were scrubbed with plenty of soap and water. Nit-infested children were cleansed, and the minor ailment clinic dealt with troubles of the skin, ears, eyes and teeth, sometimes in the same room and all at the same time.

These clinics provided a very important supportive service for the medical care of children until the coming of the National Health Service.

It was also about this time that the maternity and child welfare service came into being. This emerged as the result of three quite separate developments. They were first, the milk depot which supplied free milk to nursing mothers, of which the first was opened in 1899 by Drew Harris the MOH of St Helens; secondly the school for nursing mothers to teach them the elements of child care – the pioneer of these was John Sykes the versatile MOH of St Pancras who opened the first of these schools in 1907; thirdly the medical clinic for infants, of which the first was opened by Stallybrass in Liverpool, also in 1907. In due course these three elements came together under one roof providing food supplements as had the milk depot, health education as had the school for nursing mothers and medical supervision of mother and children as had the medical clinic. And so the maternity and child welfare centre was born.

It will have been noticed that the initiative behind the development of this service came not from the central department but from enlightened officers. The board merely observed what was going on.

There was a considerable expansion of the maternity and child welfare service during World War I, for with the men away at the front, young mothers were left to fend for their homes and families on their own. The local health departments helped to meet their needs, so far as infant care was concerned, by setting up clinics in just about every district in the land.

The war also saw the growth of services for the detection and treatment of tuberculosis and of the venereal diseases. Long term treatment of TB in sanatoria was becoming available and this was backed by the setting up of TB dispensaries by the local authorities. For VD, very much a war-time problem, methods of diagnosis, such as the Wassermann reaction were now available, and treatment through Ehrlich's 'magic bullet', Salvarsan, was provided in local authority clinics. Both of these services were made the responsibility of the MOH.

As the war ended the local government board was swept away unwept and unlamented, at any rate by the medical officer of health to whom it had never been a friend. In 1919 the Ministry of Health was founded. The new department entered on its duties with high hopes, but the housing problem, couched in Lloyd George's catch phrase 'Homes fit for heroes', was a commitment laid upon it which was to dominate all other considerations for a decade.

And so we come to 1929, a year which marks an important landmark in our progress, for it was in that year that Parliament abolished the old Poor Law, the system of administering relief to the poor over which Chadwick had presided long before, and transferred its responsibilities *and its institutions* to the local authorities. So it was that the workhouse infirmary became the municipal hospital and under the executive charge of the MOH.

Just think of his position now. He was responsible for the traditional environmental services of water supply, sewage disposal, food control and hygiene; for the public health aspects of housing; for the control and prevention of infectious disease; for the maternity and child welfare clinics and their attendant health visitors and midwives; he was responsible for the TB dispensary and for the VD clinic; then under his other hat, he was in charge of school health. Now to all this was added the responsibility for the administration of the local hospital. The MOH was now at the height of his power: this was the peak of his career and was the position that he was to hold for all but 20 years until the coming of the National Health Service.

In 1939 war came again and the MOH was immediately involved in the large-scale evacuation of children from the towns to the greater security of the countryside, and later on in coping with the effect of the bombing of the cities. In this he found himself stretched as never before, for in addition to the management of local casualty services and coordination with hospitals, he still retained his responsibility for providing the ordinary public health services for a population living and working under very difficult and abnormal conditions.

Fears of large-scale epidemics were met by a massive stepping-up of the immunisation programme, and of mass x-ray, all of which bore fruit not only then but later.

When the war ended, thoughts were turned to the framing of a National Health Service conceived as a comprehensive system for the prevention as well as the treatment of disease. The hope expressed by the medical officers of health that these services should be provided through the local authorities was not to be fulfilled. Under the tripartite structure which was set up on 5 July 1948, preventive and curative medicine went their separate ways, and the MOH lost his hospitals.

This caused something like dismay at first, but as the country moved into the post-war period it brought for the MOH new opportunities, new challenges and, let's face it, disappointment too, all of which were to tax his resources and his resourcefulness to the full.

The opportunities came with the need to provide caring and supportive services for the increasing numbers of old people in the community, and also for the physically and mentally handicapped. The challenges came with the changing pattern of disease as the infectious diseases of the past gave way to what we may call the behaviour-based diseases and the chronic conditions of the present. All this demanded new approaches, and the development of new methods of detection and prevention. This was 'modern public health'.

But I mentioned disappointment. This came in 1970 when with the implementation of the Seebohm report, social work, now recognised as a profession in its own right, was hived off to a new independence leaving the public health department shorn of its social workers. So the MOH lost half his staff with their tasks and interests and, incidentally, lost half his budget.*

---

* This proportion refers to combined health and welfare departments; not all health departments had responsibility for welfare services. (eds)

But this man was nothing if not resilient and towards the end we saw him building bridges across to general practice through the attachment of his remaining health visitors and nurses to GPs as they moved into group practice and into health centres.

And so we come nearer to our own day. In his lifespan of about a century and a quarter the MOH witnessed profound social, economic and demographic changes in our society, changes which influenced and in turn were influenced by, the health of the people he served. Let us remind ourselves of some of them. Since Duncan took up his appointment in 1847 the population of the country has almost trebled, the birth rate has fallen by more than half, the crude death rate has been cut by half, infant mortality is only one-tenth of what it was at the beginning, and the expectation of life of a male at birth has increased from 40 to nearly three score years and ten.

These figures reflect some of the changes, the improvements, in the quantity and quality of life which took place through this period and to which the MOH made his own contribution.

How then can we sum up the life story of this man, the medical officer of health? Conceived by Chadwick, born in Liverpool, he grew up in London and served his apprenticeship there. Thereafter his work took him to every corner of the kingdom. Wherever dirt and disease were to be found, he was there, and he continued to be there until ... what happened?

What happened on that night of 31 March 1974? Did he die of old age? Did he retire in the fullness of years, his work done? Was he cut off in his prime? Or did he stay in business and simply change the sign over the shop? Even now we cannot tell, but this we know, that on the following morning – it was All Fool's Day – a new man appeared on the scene calling himself the community physician, and claiming to practise not public health, but a new specialty that he called community medicine. A new man, a new specialty? Perhaps. For if we look down at his feet we shall see that he is standing in the well-worn shoes of the familiar figure the MOH. We watch with interest and concern as, wearing those shoes, he steps out on the path to take up the unending task of tackling the health problems that beset our society, the task which formed the life's work of the medical officer of health – 'a man who did honour to his profession'.

The closing passage of John Simon's first annual report, 1849:

'Gentlemen, the history of the City of London is full of great examples of public service. It records many a generous struggle for the Country and for the Constitution; it records a noble patronage of arts and letters; it records imperial magnificence and Christian liberality; but never, within the scope of its annals, has the Corporation had so grand an opportunity as now for the achievement of an unlimited good. Because of the City's illustrious history, and because of the vast wealth and power which have enabled it so often to undertake the largest measures of public utility and patriotism, – therefore it is, that the expectations of the country may well be fixed on the City of London in regard of this, the distinguishing movement of modern times – the movement to improve the social condition, and to prolong the lives of the poor.'

EPILOGUE

Public health: the decline and restoration of the tradition

by Huw Francis

INTRODUCTION

'Just think of his position now. He was responsible for the traditional environmental services of water supply, sewage disposal, food control and hygiene; for the public health aspects of housing; for the control and prevention of infectious disease; for the maternity and child welfare clinics and their attendant health visitors and midwives; he was responsible for the TB dispensary and for the VD clinic; then . . . he was in charge of school health. Now to all this was added the responsibility for the administration of the local hospital. The MOH was now at the height of his power: this was the peak of his career . . .'[1]

So Sidney Chave described the medical officer of health (MOH) during what is sometimes called the 'golden age of public health', between the passing of the Local Government Act, 1929 and the implementation of the National Health Service Act, 1946.[2] He was writing within a then well-understood and long-established historiographical convention, that of making the MOH central to telling how public health services developed.

The forces and influences which led to the beginnings of the public health movement and which shaped the various periods of change and reform were complex. Focusing on the MOH simplified the historian's task, but it employed two figures of speech: personification and synecdoche. Personification, which Sidney Chave used with subtlety and skill, added drama and pace to narration. But within the history of public health itself, it served a practical purpose also. As the

133

history of the regiment is used to promote morale, so medical officers of health (MOsH), frustrated by the apathy of their burgesses about health problems but encouraged by the achievements of Duncan, Simon and a host of witnesses, were 'baffled to fight better'. The synecdoche (the part representing the whole) was double. The powers which Sidney Chave summarises were, with a few exceptions, not those of the MOH himself,[3] but of the MOH as the servant of the local authority. The MOH was not the only member of staff of the health authority, however. All MOsH had as their colleagues the predecessors of the present environmental health officers, and in the major health authorities the health visitors, district nurses and midwives, and members of other health professions. The synecdoche puts the MOH as agent in place of the elected authority, and as leader of a diverse team in place of the team and its varied members. This figure of speech depended for its force on the reader being aware of a larger dimension, of what was not being said, of what was implied. There is no more significant indication of the decline of the old public health tradition than that few contemporary community physicians, other than the diminishing cohort of former public health medical officers, are aware that what is focal in such a narrative is not the whole story; the tacit framework has been largely forgotten. Any account of the fall of the MOH must, therefore, deal with that fall within the decline of the public health tradition as a whole.

THE DEVELOPMENT OF BRITISH SOCIAL MEDICINE

Social medicine was said by John Grant, a distinguished former medical member of staff of the Rockefeller Foundation to be:

> '. . . the study of the effect on physical or mental health of social conditions – hereditary, environmental, domiciliary, occupational and economic – and the application of that study to the preserving or restoring of health'.[4]

134

Grant was paraphrasing a definition by Sir Allen Daley, county medical officer of the old London County Council. The definition has two parts: investigative (or descriptive) and practical (normative). This division of social medicine has been the norm through much of its history, as was set out in the period immediately after the 1939–45 war, both by the American historian George Rosen's study of the genesis of the concept,[5] and the magisterial study published in English translation as *The advance to social medicine*,[6] by René Sand, at that time professor of social medicine in Brussels. This two-part definition was anticipated by John Simon (later Sir John) in his great first report as MOH to the City of London. He was appointed on 19 October 1848 and on 31 October he presented to the Court of Sewers (the nearest body then to a health committee) a scheme for the organisation of his office. His biographer, writing in 1963, rightly said that it sketched out 'what still, despite much elaboration, remains the basic organisation of the local Medical Officership of Health'.[7] It was based on two principles: what Simon called coordination and subordination. Coordination meant the collecting of accurate information, while subordination described the need for staff to investigate and pursue the remedying of 'sanitary defects';[8] Simon saw his task as both investigative and managerial. It is little wonder that in the Heath Clark Lectures for 1946, Major Greenwood, the Emeritus Professor of Epidemiology at the London School of Hygiene and Tropical Medicine, hailed as among the pioneers of British social medicine the pioneers of English public health: Chadwick, Farr and Simon.[9] In the light of this, what happened to the MOsH and English public health after 1945 was, in two ways, paradoxical.

Over-impressed, perhaps, by the rise of technology and its increasing cost in the treatment of acute illness, and the relatively lower provision for other vulnerable groups, we now tend to forget that the National Health Service and the related provisions of the welfare state were widely regarded as expressions of social medicine in practice.[10,11] As such it might have been expected that the MOsH would have played a great part in subsequent developments. The White Paper

135

prepared by HU Willink, Minister of Health in Churchill's coalition government, proposed giving local control of a national health service to elected local government.[12] Amongst others the British Medical Association opposed this strongly. Guy Dain, chairman of the association, said in summary of its views: 'We do not wish to be employed by local authorities, nor to be subject to clinical direction . . .'.[13]

This dual unpopularity probably arose from four factors. First, the decreasing respect for local authorities amongst ordinary citizens from the beginning of this century. Second, the 1929 Local Government Act had bestowed authority without means onto local government and its MOsH, since no sooner was the act on the statute book than the country was plunged into the Depression, and the consequent retrenchment of public spending. Sir George Godber has written generously of the achievements of some MOsH at this time,[14] but it has to be faced that to all but the largest and wealthiest councils, Parliament had given not power but its simulacrum. Third, there is some evidence that the hierarchical structure of the municipal hospital service had not been handled everywhere with the relaxed good humour which is required to bring out the best in high-spirited and well-qualified younger colleagues. Fourth, some teaching hospital consultants found, when seconded to peripheral hospitals, both municipal and voluntary, under the war-time Emergency Medical Service, that treatment in places had been of poor quality. Thus a surgeon was able to return many chronically sick elderly men home after simple prostatectomies, and a physician found many dying from Addisonian anaemia, who had not been given liver extract which was then the treatment of choice.[15] It would be wrong to assume that most municipal hospitals were as deprived as that, but sufficient were for it to affect the general professional view. Be this as it may, when the NHS was established by the Attlee government, the hospitals were placed under the regional hospital boards, general practice remained under the executive councils, and the local authorities were left with their sanitary powers, but the major authorities losing their hospitals were given significant additional powers for prevention, care and after-care under Part III of the National Health Service Act, 1946.[14]

Analagous changes took place in the universities and medical schools also. FAE Crew, the professor of public health (later social medicine) in Edinburgh, said in 1948 'It should be acknowledged frankly that public health, the forerunner of social medicine, has steadily lost status during the last twenty years or so . . .'.[16] This section began with the argument that public health and social medicine were identical, but it was in Britain in the 1940s that a distinction began to be drawn. John Ryle, the first professor of social medicine in the UK, in an influential book, *Changing disciplines*, published in 1948, attempted to draw a sharp distinction between social medicine and public health. It is a long passage of which two parts will be quoted:

'Public health, although in its modern practice attaching an ever-increasing importance to the personal services, for a long time and at first for very sufficient reasons, placed the emphasis on the *environment*. Social medicine, deriving its inspiration more from the field of clinical experience and seeking always to assist the discovery of a common purpose for the remedial and preventive services, places the emphasis on *man* and endeavours to study him in and in relation to his environment . . .' [Ryle's italics]

'Public health, in the first instance, and again for obvious reasons, has been largely preoccupied with the communicable diseases, their causes, distribution, and prevention. Social medicine is concerned with all diseases of prevalence, including rheumatic heart disease, peptic ulcers. . .'[17]

It is necessary to note that this is based on Ryle's centennial discourse to the New York Academy of Medicine in March 1947, when MOsH and public health departments were still exercising authority over the municipal hospitals, and was therefore inaccurate. But it sought to draw a distinction where there was no difference, for what is the actual difference between placing 'emphasis on the environment' since public health could not ignore the human dimension, and studying man 'in and in relation to his environment'? Ryle was attempting to give substance to a change which was already taking place in universities. The Goodenough report on medical schools had in 1944 recommended the replacement of departments of public health with those of social medicine.[18] The aim of this report was to create a broader undergraduate medical curriculum less narrowly determined by the various specialist and research interests. There was a seed planted by Ryle's thinking. Fred Grundy, then holding the chair of preventive medicine in Cardiff, saw in Ryle speaking of the 'discipline of social medicine' and of 'social pathology' a much narrower application of the term social medicine, as referring 'essentially to the epidemiological method'.[19] It is reasonably certain that Ryle himself did not intend this. It is easier to see his social medicine as the extension into the community of the holistic attitude he espoused in studying individual disease,[20] but it is possible to read him differently. This narrower line became the route along which social medicine tended to go. So it is not surprising by hindsight to find McKeown and Lowe, in the first edition of their influential textbook on social medicine defining it as follows:

'In contemporary usage social medicine has two meanings, one broad and ill-defined, the other more restricted and precise. In the broad sense, social medicine is an expression of the humanitarian tradition in medicine, and people read into it any interpretation consistent with their experience and interests. Thus it may be identified with humane care of patients, prevention of disease, health education, the work of local health authorities, finance of medical services; indeed with almost any subject in the extensive field of health and welfare. But in the more restrictive sense in which we shall be using the term, social medicine is concerned with a body of knowledge and methods of obtaining knowledge appropriate to a discipline. This discipline may be said to comprise (a) *epidemiology* and (b) *the study of medical needs of society*.' [McKeown and Lowe's italics][21]

Smith, a one-time colleague of McKeown's in Birmingham, has a narrower definition of social medicine,[22] but takes the exclusion of public health from the field of social medicine a step further:

> 'Thus preventive medicine became closely associated in the public and professional mind with public or community health. As an academic discipline, social medicine is the heir to public health and in medical schools has often inherited also the associated title implying an especial concern with preventive medicine.'

> *'There are several reasons why the particular association is no longer useful.* The first is that preventive medicine is no longer uniquely distinguishable as being a public concern. All medicine is now generally accepted as being involved with the public health, and provision of all kinds of health and medical care is accepted in most communities as a general social concern.' [My italics][23]

Of course at the time this was written, preventive medicine in several important senses was still 'uniquely distinguishable as being a public concern' by being embodied in the philosophy of the public health service. The impression of disassociation given by this passage is reinforced by the brief historical section which gives the pioneers of epidemiology – Snow, Budd and others – as the pioneers of 'community health' while the names of the pioneers of public health – Chadwick, Southwood Smith, Duncan, Kaye-Shuttleworth, and Simon – are notable by their absence.[24] In an essay published as recently as 1985 Smith implies that MOsH were wrong to forsake 'since the early years of the century . . . their consultative roles as community physicians in order to assume the responsibility for the day-to-day direction of extensive personal services . . .'.[25] Of course, as has been seen from the work of Simon in the City, MOsH were executive from the first, and certainly no one close to MOsH should have failed to have noticed their continuing advisory role until 1974. This view rejects the larger part of the work of the MOsH throughout their history.

At the time these were written in the mid-1960s, there

were several chairs filled with distinction by practising MOsH – Wofinden in Bristol, Semple in Liverpool – and others by full-time academics with a public health background. Most notable was Colin Frazer Brockington, whose historical scholarship was outstanding and who had just retired from the Manchester chair. These shoots from Ryle's thought were not to flower fully until the late 1970s when a high proportion of chairs came to be filled by research epidemiologists. This reductive trend in present day community medicine is well represented by Smith's 1985 essay which appears to see epidemiology as its scientific basis, suggesting that the service field is related to academic epidemiology rather as the design of binoculars and microscopes relies on the study of optics.[25]

While this trend is regrettable, the desire of academic epidemiologists to present themselves as being narrowly scientific can be understood. The funding of departments of social and community medicine by the University Grants Committee has never been sufficiently generous to provide adequate staffs. All academic departments have had to rely on research monies from the Medical Research Council and other grant-giving bodies. For most of the period under review social and community medicine has had to compete against the 'harder' medical sciences like genetics and molecular biology. The situation was eased for part of the time by specific 'research and development' funds being made available first by the central departments and then through the research councils. The restriction of public spending by the Thatcher administration has hit academic community medicine as hard as the rest of higher education. There is an unavoidable element of opportunism in applying for research funds, but the short-term gains for academic community medicine are not necessarily beneficial for the discipline as a whole.

The MOsH in the 1930s, as described by Sidney Chave, might be seen as representing, in terms of their own time, a holistic concept of social medicine. The personal standing of many should, therefore, have led them to expect a fuller share of the professional rewards of the post-war advance in social provision for health and in medical training. The management of hospitals was removed from their control, and academic social medicine developed in an unanticipated direction. Part III of the 1946 NHS Act offered for the first time an opportunity to create comprehensive schemes for the prevention, care and after-care of illness,[14] and with the improving economic circumstances of these years the legal powers were combined with reasonable finance – the substance and not the simulacrum of power. It is my view that these years, between 1945 and 1974, are the true 'golden age' of English public health, because the achievements in both the environmental and personal health services were considerable and general.[14]

In spite of all this, the status of public health declined within the medical profession, since public health doctors had been switched to a branch line separated from the main lines of professional advancement through the NHS. It has to be asked if the elected local authorities which the MOsH served would have served the hospitals better than the centralised control imposed in 1948. The NHS under its present central administration has made spectacular improvements in health care throughout the country. This is far from saying that there is no place for criticism. It is, however, possible that the hospital service would have done at least as well under local government control, and in some respects better. A high proportion of local authorities had plans for rebuilding their hospitals at the end of the 1930s; had not the war intervened and the NHS been created, many new hospitals would have been built in the 1940s and 1950s. When services which were under local authority control in the post-war era (like school building), or in which there was collaboration between central and local government (like the construction of trunk roads and motorways) are considered, it cannot be said categorically that the hospitals would have fared less well; after all the local health services made marked progress under local councils. This is speculation. What is certain is that when the doctors who began in the public health services in the 1930s reflected on their careers, they found their situation in the 1960s full of paradox. But the greatest paradox of all was yet to come.

INFLUENCES FOR FURTHER CHANGE

The welfare state was a great social and administrative experiment, and because it was experimental its original administrative structure has to be regarded as having been provisional. The influences which presaged further change and which affected the MOsH under the first phase of the welfare state, from the 1946 NHS Act to the re-organisation of the health and local government services in 1974 were closely interwoven, and there is no neat way of teasing out the strands for ordered display. They may be grouped under three headings: the growth of professionalism, a change of philosophy and reforms of administration.

Professionalism grew in the NHS and local government in two ways. New professions and vocations were established to meet newly defined needs, and both these and the established professions sought to raise their status by means of improved training and qualifications. The expansion of higher education in the 1960s assisted this process, and further stimulated it. MOsH encouraged these developments as they concerned public health staff. But the growth of professionalism led to a demand for greater freedom of action. Local authorities were, and are still, characterised by professionalised departments, hierarchically organised, within each of which there is a dominant profession from which the chief officer and senior staff are recruited,[26] a system felt to be invidious by professions which are not dominant. MOsH as heads of complex departments were particularly affected by this. The chief public health inspectors of Coventry and of Basildon achieved independence of the MOH during this period, and many of their colleagues in other authorities became chief officers while remaining under the general supervision of the MOH; this was a most important set of precedents.

There was unrest amongst other members of staff too, and the fact that some professions – like social workers and nurses – were largely composed of women added a feminist element.[27] Social workers were the focus of the greatest disruption of public health departments before 1974, and this change began earlier than any other. As the result of the death in 1945 of a boy under the care of the Shropshire county health department, the Curtis committee was set up, whose report[28] led to the Children's Act, 1945, and the creation of local authority children's departments, taking certain categories of deprived children out of the supervision of MOsH. Local authorities subsequently had groups of social workers in children's, education, welfare and health departments. After the Seebohm report,[29] MOsH of major authorities lost their power under mental health legislation, mainly to the new departments of social services.

Part of the rhetoric used by the advocates of this change was particularly damaging to the legitimate ambitions of public health medical officers. MOsH, being doctors, were said to be 'organic' in their orientation and were insufficiently aware of and sensitive to the social and emotional needs of people. As a result of this calumny, of the many public health doctors who were well qualified by personality, experience and contributions to the advance of mental health and other social services, two only – Meredith Davies in Liverpool and Dennison in Newham – were appointed directors of the new departments.

Concern about the poor performance of British industry led to a drive for better management training. The efficiency of public organisations (the civil service, local government and the NHS) was closely questioned also, both in respect of their staff and the appropriateness of their structure. All the major political parties were concerned about managerial efficiency. The Conservative party held a high-level consultation in Selsdon, near Croydon, and the term 'Selsdon man' was coined to characterise the party's managerialism. The Heath administration's reforms of local government and the NHS in 1974 were to a large part a quest for smoother, more cost-effective organisation.[30] In terms of the staff of these organisations, it was felt that a chief executive officer accountable to his or her authority for managerial performance was imperative. In local government the chief executive was introduced following the Bains report;[31] in the reform of the NHS the idea suffered a temporary defeat. The emphasis on management indicates a change of philosophy. The work of the MOH and his fellow chief officers had three

143

boundaries: the wishes of the party in power, and the limits imposed by law and finance. Managerialism at best led to a more prudent and swift conduct of business, at worst it became an overarching set of values which saw the characteristic ethics of the various professions and the rights of citizens as obstacles to efficiency.

The tripartite structure of the NHS was felt by many to be an obstacle to an efficient service, especially in continuity of care of patients who required help from more than one part. Strenuous efforts were made by MOsH of counties and county boroughs, with the support of their authorities, to overcome the gaps and duplication in services which occurred between family doctors and the local authority. The main features were the attachment of health visitors, district nurses and midwives to general practices, and the building of health centres.[14,32] Other initiatives linked the local authorities to the regional hospital boards. The outcome both of dissatisfaction with the divided structure and a wish to extend this burgeoning ecumenism was a strong drive to unify the three arms. After the Porritt report of 1962 it became the accepted wisdom within the medical profession.[33] It would also be seen as an example of the search for greater managerial efficiency. For local government structural change was advocated in a move towards larger units. The phrase 'economies of scale' was frequently used in the advocacy of the abolition of small units of local democracy. On 1 April 1974 local government (outside London) and the NHS were re-organised.

1974 AND AFTER

The re-organisation of 1974 was undertaken under two acts of Parliament: the Local Government Act, 1972, and the NHS Re-organisation Act, 1973, after preparatory work by a royal commission[34] and official committees. In England the NHS was unified under regional and area health authorities (AHAs) which were appointed bodies. The largest areas were divided into districts. About one third of the areas were small and were not so divided; these were the 'single district areas'. The family doctors, dentists, opticians and pharmacists were responsible to the family practitioner committee which was an organ of the area. Collaboration with local government was to be fostered by the AHAs being coterminous with the metropolitan district authorities in the large conurbations, and elsewhere with the shire counties. There was no chief executive, but the management, under each authority, was by teams of officers who worked by consensus. In regions and the larger areas the teams consisted of an administrator, a treasurer, a nurse and a community physician. In the districts and the single district areas a hospital consultant and a family doctor elected by peers were added.[35]

There were two major criticisms of these arrangements: there was one administrative tier too many, and with consensus management decision-making and the dispatch of business could be slow. Consensus management carried much of the blame due to the delays caused by the elaborate consultative procedures built into the planning process, and to the restrictions of finance; but there was more than an element of truth in the criticisms.

The Thatcher administration dealt with these points in two stages. In 1982 one tier of the NHS was removed. The 'geographical' area tier was abolished, and the powers of areas devolved to new district authorities. The family practitioner committees remained unchanged, but became independent of local administration. Under the districts, a new pattern of unit administration was established. In 1984–5 consensus management was replaced by general managers in regions, districts and units, effectively implementing the objective of the Heath administration of chief executives in health authorities. The changes in local government, while considerable, can for the purposes of this essay be dealt with briefly since we are interested mainly in the 'collaboration function'. The metropolitan districts within the great conurbations are, in local government terms, 'all-purpose authorities'; the former AHAs had responsibilities towards them which were comprehensive. In the shire counties, the AHA dealt with the county authority and the health district related to the elected county district councils but they were not necessarily coterminous. The removal of the AHAs in 1982 made the problems of collaboration more complicated, since most shire counties and some large metropolitan districts now contain more than one health authority.

It is not sufficiently appreciated how vast was the change in 1974. It was probably the largest constitutional change in terms of the elected bodies and officers affected, and possibly the most significant after the crisis over Lloyd George's 'People's budget' of 1910 and, more recently, the legislation for entry to the EEC. The future of the MOH and of the public health service, however important in itself, was not central to the restructuring of local administration, but was a problem which resulted from it. The effects on the public health services have been severe and will be traced in the change from the MOH to the community physician, the break-up of the public health team and the downgrading of the public health tradition.

After 1948 there were three loosely associated groups of doctors: the public health medical officers, the senior administrative medical officers and their medical staffs, and the doctors within the academic departments of social medicine. The Royal Commission on Medical Education recommended the unification of the discipline. It suggested the name 'community medicine' and the philosophy of dealing with 'groups and not individuals'; it also recommended the creation of a new professional body to help to unify the field.[36] After prolonged and difficult negotiations, however, the Faculty of Community Medicine of the Royal Colleges of Physicians of the United Kingdom was created in 1972. The conception of community medicine was to be incarnated in the community physician.[32] The first full exposition came from Professor Jeremy Morris (Sidney Chave's head of department and friend). Morris saw the community physician as an administrator of local services, as epidemiologist and as adviser to his local community – qualitatively different from the MOH, but retaining noteworthy public health elements.[37]

In translating these ideas into the unified NHS the Hunter

report[38] together with the 'Grey Book'[35] are the most important studies. The community physician was seen as a medical specialist alongside other medical specialists, as a manager within the NHS and as an 'adviser to and a manager of services for local government'.[39] This reflected the thinking of the parallel study on collaboration between the NHS and local government.[40] All three bodies saw that the local authorities would require advice on school health, personal health services, and environmental health. In the 1974 re-organisation community physicians were appointed as regional and area medical officers and district community physicians within the consensus management teams. Additional specialists were appointed, at region mainly distributed by the functions of management – information, planning, personnel and so on – and at area (other than for information and planning) by the local authority functions – school health service, social services and environmental health. Those community physicians whose work included environmental health carried the title 'medical officer for environmental health' (MOEH).

The public health doctors were thus transferred to the NHS. The social workers had departed in 1970. What happened to the rest of the team, especially the two particularly involved in prevention – health visitors and EHOs? In 1974 the nurses, including the health visitors, were transferred to the hierarchically organised NHS nursing service under the area and district nursing officers. The EHOs stayed with local government. Before the re-organisation there was a mass of sanitary law which the MOH and EHO administered on behalf of the local authority, and which in 1974 remained the responsibility of local government. The MOH was removed from the statute book by amendments under section 180 and schedule 14, and by repeals under section 272 and schedule 30, Local Government Act, 1972; these were the hilt and blade of the dirk which gave the MOH his quietus. Fired by the example of the chief public health inspectors of Coventry and Basildon, the EHOs had made a bid for freedom, but it did not work out that way. The Bains committee issued in 1971 an interim report, which was reflected in the 1972 act.[41] It recommended the removal of the protected status of certain officers who could not be dismissed without the agreement of the appropriate Minister. Thus senior EHOs lost this security.[42] The main Bains report suggested that environmental health should be associated with other services, broadly environmental – refuse collection, coast protection, markets and so on. Now, only in a minority of local authorities are chief EHOs heads of department. Nor are the heads of environmental services departments always members of the management teams of senior officers who advise the chief executive. Environmental health has therefore lost status within the local authorities; and both health visitors and EHOs, seeking greater freedom, found they had exchanged one form of bondage for another.

All in all 1974 was a crisis for the MOH in which almost all elements of the structure which supported his unique role disappeared. The crisis also affected the professional and local authority related national organisations associated with the public health functions of local authorities. The Society of Medical Officers of Health, the main professional society of public health medical officers, squeezed by the loss of members and rising costs, slimmed down its organisation and changed its name to the Society of Community Medicine in 1973. The Royal Society of Health and the Royal Institute of Public Health and Hygiene which for many years had arranged large annual conferences and other meetings for elected members and officers of local authorities were seen to be less relevant to the work of local government and the NHS, and rapidly declined. The three bodies, which still exist, are now but shards of their previous glory.

The cohort of former public health medical officers diminishes within the service year by year; but this natural wastage has been accelerated by the premature retirement of experienced doctors at each of the reorganisations in 1972, 1982 and currently under the Griffiths proposals.[43] The medical staff of the old Ministry of Health and the DHSS at one time had extensive public health experience – people like Neil Beattie (one of the originators of the term 'community physician'[32]) or the great expert on infectious disease, WH Bradley. The able younger doctors who replaced them had had their experience mainly in hospitals and general practice; the dialogue between centre and periphery, though continuing to be valuable, changed subtly, especially after 1974.

The most marked effect followed the narrowing of the academic field of community medicine. The doctors from public health and academic social medicine who were involved with others in preparations for the change in the early 1970s were almost without exception people of very broad vision. The MOsH who took part in setting up the Faculty of Community Medicine and its early boards were people of outstanding achievement like Wilfred Harding (Camden), Tom Galloway (West Sussex), John Warin (Oxford) and Ronald Elliott (West Riding of Yorkshire). The syllabus for the membership of the faculty, influenced considerably by Michael Warren, its first academic registrar, included much that was relevant to the public health function. The foundational documents of the NHS specialty of community medicine – the Hunter[38] and Collaboration reports[40] and the 'Grey Book'[35] – emphasised the public health aspects, and environmental health was a particular concern.[44] In spite of this the changes of 1974 created a great sense of anxiety, a feeling of matters being not fully under control and of an intellectual void. In this scene the academic departments were least affected, and were able to exert a degree of leadership which might not have been theirs had the change been evolutionary and gradual. The result has been a marked reductionism in the philosophy of many community physicians. Jane Lewis in her survey of their attitude to their role found that:

> 'Academic members of the Faculty have tended to emphasise community medicine's status as a fully fledged medical specialty and to draw an analogy between the practice of clinical and population medicine in a manner similar to John Ryle, the first professor of social medicine in the 1940s. The natural correlate of this has been the emphasis placed on the specialty's skill base in epidemiology and therefore on its advisory role.'[45]

Lewis cites Smith for this view,[46] and her words neatly encapsulate the viewpoint of his 1985 essay.[25] It is not surprising that Lewis found differences among the attitudes of service community physicians. Older specialists in community medicine 'saw their main responsibility in terms of running particular community health services, local authority liaison work or *the more traditional elements of public health work, such as communicable disease control*' (my italics). The younger and more recently trained group were more concerned to use their epidemiological and statistical skills in analysing the needs of their districts.[45]

It is precisely at the point of its most traditional function, the control of communicable disease, that community medicine has been under most criticism recently, after the publication of the reports on the outbreak of food poisoning at Stanley Royd Hospital, Wakefield,[47] and of Legionnaire's disease at the District General Hospital, Stafford.[48]

It is not sufficiently widely appreciated that environmental health law now allows a senior officer of the local authority, with no medical or environmental health training, to be the 'proper officer' for infectious disease control.[49] Recommendations made by official publications on important subjects, like tuberculosis[50] or viral haemorrhagic fevers[51] assume that the MOEH has the necessary legal powers. This mistake was not made by the Stafford inquiry:

> 'Evidence we heard and submissions made to us lead us to believe that the responsibilities and authority of the MOEH need to be reviewed. We also believe that there is legitimate concern that the present training and experience of MOsEH is less effective than that formerly provided to fit them to undertake responsibilities for the investigation and control of outbreaks of infections.'[52]

Thus the age-old function of the MOH has been criticised, the MOsEH lack legal power and community physicians everywhere have been displaced under Griffiths. The zenith of epidemiological reductionism in the academic field has coincided with the nadir of the fortunes of service community physicians in the NHS and local government.

Yet the greatest paradox is that from this lowest point may arise the opportunity to rebuild the 'bare ruin'd choirs' of the public health tradition.

RESTORING THE TRADITION

A sea change has overtaken community medicine. In the crisis which the discipline is facing at the present time, the term 'public health' is increasingly used. Following the publication of the Stanley Royd report, the Secretary of State set up, under the chairmanship of Sir Donald Acheson, the Chief Medical Officer, an inquiry with terms of reference which include:

> 'To consider the future development of the public health function, including the control of communicable disease and the speciality of community medicine . . .'[53]

Smith, in his report as retiring president of the Faculty of Community Medicine, said that in its evidence to the Acheson committee the Faculty has 'sought to re-assert the traditional roles and values of public health doctors'.[54] Some of the younger Fellows and Members of the Faculty are talking of the new medical officer of health. This will greatly encourage all those – not only former public health doctors – who have mourned the decline of the tradition.

Two processes can be distinguished in the restoration of a tradition: its *rediscovery* and its *recovery*.[55] *Recovery* means rebuilding the institutions and practices which support a tradition. Almost all the structures on which the office of MOH stood have been dismantled, but history has many examples of the renewal of traditions in new and radically different institutional forms. In the changed circumstances of the late 1980s and the 1990s, it is not unreasonable to regard as possible the re-creation of the MOH. In an historical paper it would not be appropriate to pursue the administrative changes required. But it is clear that community medicine needs a firm base within the NHS with strong departments of community medicine at region and district.[56] The position of community physicians within

151

local authorities should be strengthened; the 'proper officer' should invariably be medically qualified. Moreover, the position of EHOs requires parallel examination. So too does the content of dialogue between the medical staff of DHSS and community physicians at the periphery.

The new MOH will not be created all at once. The office will have to be rebuilt over time as it was painstakingly built up in the first place, 'line upon line, here a little, and there a little'.

The *rediscovery* of tradition is a matter of history. The term 'public health' in its new popularity is used as if its meaning is crystal clear and unproblematic. In my experience before 1974 'public health' was used in four loosely related ways. Most broadly it meant the state of health of a defined community, national or local; in this sense it was used in the traditional title of the Chief Medical Officer's annual report, *On the state of the public health*. It was a synonym, or near synonym, for the practice of preventive medicine. Most frequently in British practice, however, it meant public provision for the prevention, care and aftercare of illness; 'public' here meant the state as represented by central and local government. (State medicine was one of the terms used at one time for public health.) Public health in this sense was used exclusively of services provided by and through local government; after 1948 it was not applied to the hospital and family practitioner services. The fourth use was in the term 'public health law', the framework of statute and common law within which these services operated, and the legal provisions they administered. Influenced by epidemiological reductionism, some community physicians tend to take the first two meanings as if they related exclusively to population medicine. The concept of community and of society which underlies the public health tradition is far richer than the demographic considerations alone which dominate the concept of population medicine. The concept of public health in Britain is vested within public administration and has its locus in administrative law. The breadth and richness of classical public health can be heard if we eavesdrop on Sir John Simon reflecting in 1890 on his annual reports as MOH of the City from 1849 onwards:

'After a lapse of so many years . . . I rejoice to remember that, even in those early days, I did my best to make clear to the commission, what sufferings and degradation were incurred by masses of the labouring population through the conditions under which they were so generally housed in courts and alleys they inhabited: not only how unwholesome were those conditions, but how shamefully inconsistent with reasonable standards of civilisation; and how vain it must be to expect good social fruit from human life running its course under such conditions'.[57]

'In referring to some of the existing evils, I of course found myself face to face with immensely difficult social questions which I could not pretend to discuss; questions as to wages and poverty and pauperism; in relation to which I could only observe, as of medical commonsense, that, if given wages will not purchase such food and such lodgement as are necessary for health, the rate-payers who bury the labourer, when starvation-disease or filth-disease has laid him low, are in effect paying the too late arrears of wage which might have hindered the suffering and sorrow'.[58]

The doctor who wrote those passages was not solely concerned with statistical or epidemiological evidence. He was not even concerned with health as an end, but as a means to an end; not simply to promote a healthy life, but a healthy, civilised life. The test of the basic attitude of MOsH is their attitude to overcrowding of dwellings. It was twofold; overcrowding increased the risk of infection and of fatal disease, but MOsH stressed even more persistently the effects of overcrowding on morality:[59]

'. . . common humanity requires that the other aspect of this evil [overcrowding] should not be ignored. For where overcrowding exists in its sanitary sense, almost always it exists even more perniciously in certain moral senses. In its higher degree it almost necessarily involves such negation of all delicacy, such unclean confusion of bodies and bodily functions, such mutual exposure of animal and sexual nakedness, as is rather bestial than human. To be subject to these influences is a degradation which must become deeper and deeper for those on whom it continues to work. To children who are born under its curse it must often be a baptism into infamy'.[60]

While the prevention of disease was at the heart of the concern of MOsH, their commitment was to a wider concern – the relief of the suffering and the deprivation of their fellow men and women.

That commitment was not expressed politically. Simon viewed the MOH first and foremost as an expert and a specialist in preventive medicine.[61] At first the public health movement was founded on the miasmatic theory of disease.[62] The miasmatic theory, while erroneous, pointed in the right direction, towards the association of disease and the environment. The views of public health doctors changed, however. In the writings of William Farr the evolution of the scientific basis of public health can be traced: the growth of knowledge of clinical medicine, the increasing sophistication of nosology and the slow steps towards the adoption of the germ theory. At each stage MOsH were concerned to apply the best scientific knowledge available. The most potent of these scientific advances was in clinical medicine itself. Public health doctors were often themselves clinicians. Simon was a surgeon at St Thomas' Hospital throughout his professional life. Many of Simon's colleagues and friends in public health were also distinguished clinicians like John Bristowe, MOH for Camberwell who was a physician at St Thomas' and Burdon Sanderson, MOH for Paddington, who as Sir John Burdon Sanderson was later Regius Professor of Medicine at Oxford. In our own time two MOsH held part-time posts as consultants in infectious diseases: John Warin of Oxford and John Kershaw of Colchester. Malcolm Pleyclell and JJA (now Sir John) Reid when in Northamptonshire added to our knowledge of Huntington's Chorea. Mary Sheridan (DHSS) and Dorothy Egan (LCC) helped to found the sub-speciality of developmental paediatrics.

An argument has been put forward which suggests that epidemiology is the dominant part of the knowledge base of community medicine.[25,63] Any specialty which deals with the planning and provision of services and with the prevention of illness in the community requires sound statistical and epidemiological information; that is a truism which needs no elaborate justification. In the control of communicable disease, a knowledge of the epidemiology is not enough. Sound clinical knowledge and judgement, and a familiarity with the relevant microbiology are essential. Indeed, the action an MOEH may take in relation to control measures may often depend on his or her clinical assessment of a case before there is time for laboratory confirmation of the diagnosis. In the non-communicable diseases, it is unwise for a community physician to pontificate on the basis of statistical or epidemiological evidence without some idea of the clinical realities. Epidemiology is necessary, but it is not sufficient and community medicine must recover the public health attitude of seeing clinical medicine and microbiology as important scientific bases of its practice of prevention.

There is a major misunderstanding of the position of the MOH, and by extension of the contemporary community physician. This is the advocacy of the community physician taking an overtly political position, and that community physicians should be given statutory protection to enable them to do so.[25,63] Simon said that the MOH:

> '. . . should hold his office during good behaviour, and should in his office be protected against the resentment of persons whom the proper discharge of his duties might be apt to offend'.[64]

The offence the MOsH were likely to cause was not primarily political, but administrative, in the routine execution of their statutory duties. Thus William Farr observed 'in certain districts in London the Medical Officer of Health is under all sorts of restraint. If he is active they look on him with disfavour, and he is in great danger of dismissal,' and *The Lancet* said that MOsH were 'in a very awkward position; if they conscientiously carry out their duties, they can hardly fail to come into conflict with the local authorities to whom they are subordinate'.[65] Simon insisted on the impartiality of the MOH:

'Each authority, endeavouring to fulfil (its) duties ... would periodically need to be furnished with a skilled impartial report on the health and the sanitary requirements of its district, and would on occasions require unbiased medical certification or advice with regard to points of current business, administrative or forensic'.[66]

('Forensic' here means requiring legal action.) On the one hand, as every senior community physician will know, a report made to an authority in pursuance of official policy and based also on carefully considered technical information and professional knowledge may lead to political objections even though it is not overtly political; or if there are no objections to the principle of the report, the expenditure involved may become a political issue. On the other hand, the balance between officers and members changed. An obituary of my former colleague, the late Sir Alec Clegg, the last chief education officer of the West Riding of Yorkshire stated, 'Politicians today would soon cut down a CEO who threatened to collect to himself the kind of authority Clegg assumed after a quarter of a century in office'.[67] This does not mean that a community physician should not get involved with controversy. The routine work will bring controversy enough and his or her advice will be more acceptable to the authority if it is well aware of the community physician's competence and impartiality. The community physicians may be consultants, but they, like the MOH, because of their involvement in administration, are also public servants. Simon and his contemporaries were among those who established a tradition of professional competence and impartiality for public servants. The more community physicians are involved with elected bodies – that is, the local authorities or health authorities if some proposals go forward – the more important is impartiality. This does not, of course, preclude the faculty or other associations of community physicians taking a political stance.

There are two other related features. Readers of Simon's *English sanitary institutions* will be impressed by the extent to which it is the history of public health legislation. MOsH could innovate only with the concurrence of their authorities and within the legal powers available. A knowledge of the law was essential. The amount of law that the MOH needed to know directly was not large, but familiarity with legislation and some skill in consulting legal sources were important. Related to law is the question of ethics. A feature of the historiography of English public health is that several of its historians see in it an expression of a new humanitarian spirit which was introduced into English society in the 18th century.[68] The 'larger sympathy of man with man' said Simon, quoting the historian John Richard Green. The same view would not be taken now by historians, but it is more important that Simon and others thought this, than that the interpretation has changed. Simon himself seems to have been influenced by the Christian Socialists; Charles Kingsley was a personal friend.[69] The Edinburgh trained public health pioneers associated with Manchester seem to have been influenced by the ethical views of the Scottish Enlightenment.[70] John Ryle taught that social medicine had an ethical background.[71] If the claim is made, as it is, that the distribution of health care should be based wholly or substantially on epidemiological considerations, it is a displacement of the ethical by the technical. For 2,500 years, since the time of Aristotle, it has been recognised that the distribution of the good things of society is at least in part an issue of ethics or distributive justice. In the pluralistic society in which we live, an awareness of the ethical issues is, perhaps, even more important.

The main purpose of history is to elucidate the continuities and discontinuities which stand between us and our past. Preventive medicine and public health cannot be fully understood without a knowledge of the historical record. Ryle and the Birmingham workers forgot that part of the meaning of any term lies in its provenance, in its past. George Rosen was critical of the lack of conceptual clarity of Ryle's and other early British definitions of social medicine.[72] Definitions may be changed, but those who desire change must engage in a fruitful dialogue with the past. What may result otherwise is a damaging caprice. Too often in contemporary community medicine literature brief historical references appear, almost always undocumented, almost always misleading. Epidemiologists should know that the random sample is not usually an instrument of historical scholarship. One of the major differences between the old public health movement and contemporary community medicine is the comparative loss of interest in its history. What can be learnt from the history of public health is a knowledge of how progress has been made, how scientific and social research has led to legislation; how epidemics and other unforeseen events have been dealt with; how human nature responds; and how the institutions of our society work. History does not repeat itself; future is not fixed by the past 'like words locked in pencils . . . like thorns locked up in seeds'. But a knowledge of history is an aid to judgement; it increases our repertoire of responses. It is the key to the door through which the restored tradition may be reached.

In writing this epilogue to this selection of the writings of my friend Sidney Chave, I have been aware not only that I have been dealing with a story Sidney knew but because of his final illness could not write down, but also that he represented the tradition itself. The decline of the public health tradition greatly saddened him, the recent revival of interest in public health would have greatly cheered him. His devotion to the history of public health, in times which were not wholly favourable, through his teaching at the London School of Hygiene and Tropical Medicine and the History of Medicine courses at the Society of Apothecaries, through his long and fruitful association with the Society for the Social History of Medicine and through his writings was unshakable. Though trained at first in the sciences, his major contribution was to the humanities which are an important part of the public health tradition. Of Sidney, as of the medical officer of health whom he celebrated, it may be said, in the words of the memorial to Sir Robert Shirley at Staunton Harold:

> Whose singular praise it is
> To have done the best things in the worst of times
> And
> Hoped them in the most calamitous.

NOTES AND REFERENCES

1 See page 127.
2 In this section I refer almost exclusively to medical officers of health and the public health service as they existed in England and Wales.
3 The masculine pronoun is used correctly. So far as I am aware there were no women MOsH of major local authorities in England and Wales at this date.
4 Grant John B. Social medicine in Western Europe (1950). Reprinted in Seipp C (ed). Health care for the community: selected papers of Dr John B Grant. Baltimore, The Johns Hopkins Press, 1963, p 42.
5 Rosen George. What is social medicine? (1947) Reprinted in Rosen George. From medical police to social medicine: essays in the history of health care. New York, Science History Publications, 1974, p 116.
6 Sand René. The advance to social medicine. London, Staples Press, 1952, p 558.
7 Lambert Royston. Sir John Simon and English social administration. London, MacGibbon and Kee, 1963, pp 114–17.
8 For Sir John Simon's own account *see* English sanitary institutions (2nd edition). London, John Murray, 1897, pp 248–58. For a later account by the local medical officer of health in Brighton *see* Sir Arthur Newsholme's similarly autobiographical work Fifty years in public health (volume 1). London, George Allen and Unwin, 1935, pp 151–9.
9 Greenwood Major. Some British pioneers of social medicine. London, Oxford University Press, 1948.
10 Grant John B. *op cit* note 4, pp 43–5.
11 Sand René. *op cit* note 5, pp 539–41 *et passim*.
12 Ministry of Health. A national health service. London, HMSO, 1944. Cmd. 6502.
13 Quoted in Goodman Neville M. Wilson Jameson: architect of national health. London, George Allen and Unwin, 1970, p 119.
14 Godber Sir George. Medical officers of health and health services. Community Medicine, 1986, 8, pp 1–14.

15 Quoted in Stevens Rosemary. Medical practice in modern England. New Haven, Yale University Press, 1966, p 68.

16 Crew FAE. Social medicine as an academic discipline. In Massey Arthur (ed). Modern trends in public health. London, Butterworth, 1949, p 76.

17 Ryle John A. Changing disciplines. London, Oxford University Press, 1948, pp 11–12.

18 Ministry of Health and Department of Health for Scotland. Report of the inter-departmental committee on medical schools. (Chairman Sir William Goodenough.) London, HMSO, 1944.

19 Grundy Fred. Preventive medicine and public health (3rd edition). London, HK Lewis, 1957, p 8.

20 Ryle John A. The physician as naturalist. In The natural history of disease (2nd edition). London, Oxford University Press, 1948, pp 1–23.

21 McKeown Thomas and Lowe CR. An introduction to social medicine. Oxford, Blackwell, 1966, p ix.

22 Smith Alwyn. The science of social medicine. London, Staples Press, 1968, pp 7–8 and 11.

23 *ibid*, p 209.

24 *ibid*, chapter 1, especially pp 17–19.

25 Smith Alwyn. The epidemiological basis of community medicine. In Smith Alwyn (ed). Recent advances in community medicine 3. Edinburgh, Churchill Livingstone, 1985, pp 1–10.

26 Greenwood Royston and Stewart JD. The institutional and organisational capabilities of local government. Public Administration, 1986, 64, 1, pp 34–50.

27 For an account of a similar conflict between a medical officer of health and a senior dental officer *see* Gelbin Stanley. Britain's first community orthodontic scheme: for the children of Heston and Isleworth. Medical History, 1985, 29, pp 414–32.

28 Great Britain, Parliament. Report of the care of children committee (Chairman Miss Myra Curtis). London, HMSO, 1946. Cmnd. 6922.

29 Report of the committee on local authority and allied

personal social services (Chairman Sir Frederick Seebohm). London, HMSO, 1968. Cmnd. 3703.

30 The reforms of the NHS and local government were undertaken under legislation put forward by the Heath administration, but were put into effect under the Wilson administration, the process of change having gone too far for the new Labour government to make more than minor modifications.

31 Department of the Environment. The new local authorities: management and structure (Chairman ME Bains). London, HMSO, 1972.

32 Francis Huw. Towards community medicine: the British experience. In Bennett AE (ed). Recent advances in community medicine 1. Edinburgh, Churchill Livingstone, 1978, pp 1–17.

33 Medical services review committee. A review of the medical services in Great Britain (Chairman Sir Arthur Porritt). London, Social Assay, 1962.

34 Report of the royal commission on local government in England 1966–1969 (Chairman The Rt Hon Lord Redcliffe-Maud). London, HMSO, 1969. Cmnd. 4040.

35 Department of Health and Social Security. Management arrangements for the re-organised National Health Service (the Grey Book). London, HMSO, 1972.

36 Report of the royal commission on medical education (Chairman Baron Todd). London, HMSO, 1968. Cmnd. 3569.

37 Morris JN. Tomorrow's community physician. The Lancet, 1969, II, 811–16.

38 Department of Health and Social Security. Report of the working party on medical administrators (Chairman Dr RB Hunter). London, HMSO, 1972.

39 The Grey Book, *op cit* note 35, pp 71–3.

40 Department of Health and Social Security and Welsh Office. A report from the working party on collaboration between the NHS and local government on its activities to the end of 1972 (the first Collaboration report). London, HMSO, 1973.

41 The study group on local authority management structures. Interim report of the working group (note 31). Department of the Environment, 1971, Appendix A, pp 130–44.

42 Senior public health inspectors enjoyed a protected status under section 110 of the Local Government Act 1933. The whole of the 1933 act was repealed by section 272 and schedule 30 of the Local Government Act 1972.

43 Department of Health and Social Security. NHS management inquiry (Leader Roy Griffiths). London, DHSS, 1983.

44 *See* the Hunter report, note 38, paras 81–4, pp 30–32; para 96, p 35; and para 109, p 39. *See also* the Collaboration report, note 40, chapter 3, pp 17–23 and Appendices B, C and D, pp 81–7 *and* the Grey Book, note 39, para 4.23, p 73; para 4.26, p 74, para 4.1, p 123 and para 5.1, p 125.

45 Lewis Jane. The changing fortunes of community medicine. Public Health, 1986, 100, pp 3–10.

46 Smith Alwyn. What do community physicians do? An academic view. In What do community physicians do? Manchester, Unit for Continuing Education, Department of Community Medicine, University of Manchester, occasional papers no 1, 1981, pp 3–10.

47 Department of Health and Social Security. The report of the committee of inquiry into an outbreak of food poisoning at Stanley Royd Hospital. London, HMSO, 1986. Cmnd. 9716.

48 Department of Health and Social Security. First report of the committee of inquiry into the outbreak of Legionnaire's disease in Stafford in April 1985. London, HMSO, 1986. Cmnd. 9772.

49 Paragraph 13, schedule 14, Local Government Act 1972 referred to 'the proper officer . . . or a registered medical practitioner'. This paragraph has been repealed by section 28 and schedule 3 of the Public Health (Control of Disease) Act 1984, subsection 3. Section 11 of the same act refers simply to the 'proper officer'. No qualification other than recognition by the local authority is required.

50 Citron KM, Raynes RH and Berrie JRH. Tuberculosis today. London, HMSO, 1981, p 30.

51 Department of Health and Social Security and the Welsh Office. Memorandum on the control of viral haemorrhagic fevers. London, HMSO, 1986, para 56, p 21.

52 Department of Health and Social Security. Note 48, para 139, p 25.

53 Department of Health and Social Security. Letter from Secretary, Committee of inquiry into future development of the public health function and community medicine. April 1986.

54 Faculty of Community Medicine. Agenda papers for the 14th annual general meeting, Cardiff, 3 July 1986.

55 Pelikan Jaruslav. The vindication of tradition. New Haven, Yale University Press, 1984, p 24.

56 John HH. The medical officer of health: past, present and future. (In press.)

57 Simon. Note 8, p 253.

58 *ibid*, p 255.

59 Wohl Anthony S. Unfit for human habitation. In Dyos HJ and Wolff Michael (eds). The Victorian city (volume 2). London, Routledge and Kegan Paul, 1973, pp 603–24.

60 Simon Sir John. Eighth report to the Privy Council. Quoted in Wohl above.

61 Simon. Note 8, pp 335–6.

62 This is an oversimplification. For a detailed account of disease theories in relation to the early public health movement *see* Pelling Margaret. Cholera, fever and English medicine 1825–1865. Oxford, Oxford University Press, 1978.

63 Faculty of Community Medicine. The role and function of the specialty of community medicine. Evidence submitted to the Acheson committee, July 1986.

64 Simon. Note 8, p 338.

65 Quoted in Wohl. Note 59, p 607.

66 Simon. Note 8, p 339. *See also* pp 335–6.

67 Maclure Stuart. The Times Educational Supplement, 24 January 1984, p 4.

68 *See* Simon. Note 8, pp 128–65. *See also* Morris Sir Malcolm. The story of English public health. London, Cassell, 1919, pp 1–13. *See also* Greenwood. Note 9, p 3.

69 Lambert. Note 7, p 34 and p 199.

70 For Percival and Kay-Shuttleworth *see* Chitnis Anand C. The Scottish enlightenment and early Victorian English society. London, Croom Helm, 1986, pp 133–79. On the ethical teaching *see* Sher Richard B. Church and university in the Scottish enlightenment. Edinburgh, Edinburgh University Press, 1985, pp 166–212.

71 Ryle. Note 17, pp 101–19.

72 Rosen. Note 5, pp 108–11.

ANNOTATED BIBLIOGRAPHY

The history of public health

Compiled by Dorothy Watkins, The Wellcome Institute for the History of Medicine, London

GENERAL HISTORIES

Brockington CF **Public health in the nineteenth century** Edinburgh, Churchill Livingstone, 1965. General history which contains some unique information on the first MOsH appointed between 1848 and 1856.

Frazer William M **A history of English public health, 1834–1939** London, Baillière, Tindall and Cox, 1950. Seminal reference work written during the modern period. Frazer's comprehensive study matches the most important legislation with the people who made and executed it.

Rosen George **The history of public health** New York, MD Publications, 1958. A historically broad and immensely erudite comparison of public health systems in societies from antiquity to modernity.

Wohl Anthony **Endangered lives** London, Methuen, 1984. An economic and social analysis of the features of Victorian society which created a physical environment that threatened the lives of its subjects.

BIOGRAPHIES

Eyler John **Victorian social medicine. The ideas and methods of William Farr** Baltimore, Johns Hopkins, 1979. William Farr, compiler of abstracts at the Registrar General's office was responsible for introducing the use of statistics of mortality and disease incidence into the policy-making process of the Victorian state. This is a useful reference work on a crucial figure of the early and mid-century.

Finer SE **The life and times of Edwin Chadwick** London, Methuen, 1952. This account of the life and work of the founder of public health in Victorian England provides an excellent analysis of the utilitarian politics which guided health reform. Finer documents the early years of the health movement with detailed precision, relating ideas, and ideals, to individuals, voluntary organisations and parliamentary process.

Frazer WM **Duncan of Liverpool** London, Hamilton Medical Books, 1947. William Duncan, the first medical officer of health, was appointed under a local act at Liverpool in 1846. Frazer demonstrates the influence which Duncan's pioneering work had upon both national and local politics.

Lambert Royston **Sir John Simon 1816–1904 and English sanitary administration** London, Macgibbon and Kee, 1963. Lambert's biography is the finest study of the rise of state medicine in the administration of the public health system during the mid-Victorian period. Simon's career is contextualised firmly within his achievements and failures and the structure of opposition.

LOCAL ADMINISTRATION AND MEDICAL OFFICERS

Brand Jeanne **Doctors and the state. The British medical profession and government action in public health, 1870–1912** Baltimore, Johns Hopkins, 1965. An examination of the role of medical men in the relationship between local and central government regarding health care before 1911. Both Poor Law and public health are discussed in this context.

Chave Sidney, Francis Huw, Waring J and Wofinden R C. **Proceedings of the Royal Society of Medicine**. A collection of articles on the historical transformation of the role of medical officers of health to that of community physicians, 67, 1974, pp 1243–55.

Wilkinson (Hardy) Ann **The beginnings of disease control in London: the work of medical officers in three parishes, 1856–1900** Oxford, PhD thesis, 1982. The first detailed examination of local public health departments. The economic analysis of intervention on the health of the parish populations of Camberwell, Newington and St Georges-the-Martyr is without parallel for any other sanitary district.

Watkins Dorothy E **The English revolution in social medicine** London, PhD thesis, 1984. The professionalisation of preventive medicine is examined through a prosopography of all metropolitan MOsH appointed before 1911; by following the development of the DPH; through a study of the manuscript records of the Society of Medical Officers of Health; in a survey of the journals associated with prevention; and an analysis of the content of the 19th century textbooks on public hygiene.

STUDIES ON STATE MEDICINE, PREVENTIVE MEDICINE AND SOCIAL MEDICINE

Primary sources (listed chronologically)

Frank JP **A system of complete medical police** (Translated from 3rd edition, 1756; edited by Erna Lesky). Baltimore, Johns Hopkins, 1976. This was the first analytical work on the creation of measures to be taken with regard to public safety as far as they concern public health.

Chadwick Edwin **Report from the Poor Law commissioners on an enquiry into the sanitary condition of the labouring population of Great Britain** (Edited by MW Flinn) Edinburgh, Edinburgh University Press, 1965. The first national survey of environmental health conditions which guided the Public Health Act 1848.

Virchow R **Collected essays on public health and epidemiology** (2 vols, translated from *Gesammelte abhandlungen aus dem Gebiete der offentlichen Medizin und der Seuchenlehre*, 1879, edited by LJ Rather) New York, Science History Publications, 1985. This recent translation of the public health essays (written largely during the 1840s and published in 1879) by the founder of cellular pathology who was equally important to the foundation of social medicine is an invaluable reference work. The essays illustrate the contemporary and comparative context in which the English system developed.

Rumsey HW **Essays on state medicine** London, Churchill, 1856. A definitive text on the concept of state medicine in England, which dominated the mid-Victorian period.

Simon J **English sanitary institutions** London, Melbourne, Castle and Company, 1890. Simon's political and economic vision of public health, documented by a massive amount of factual information extracted from the many reports completed for his department during his period as medical officer to the Privy Council.

Newman George **The rise of preventive medicine** London, Oxford University Press, 1932. The first medical officer to the first Ministry of Health outlined his perspective on the historical events which led to the rise of preventive medicine from antiquity, in the Heath Clarke lecture series.

Newman George **The health of the state** London, Social Services Handbooks, 1907. A preview of Newman's image of national health which he developed further in his Charles Hastings lecture delivered in 1928, 'The foundation of national health' (London, 1928).

Newsholme Arthur **The last fifty years in public health: a personal narrative with comments. The years preceding 1909** London, Allen and Unwin, 1935. *Idem* **The last thirty years in public health: recollections and reflections on my official and post official life** London, Allen and Unwin, 1936. Newsholme's professional autobiographies contain far more than simply a personal narrative. His career spanned both local and central government, being first the MOH for Brighton and leading member of the Society of Medical Officers of Health and latterly the medical officer to the Local Government Board during the period leading up to the formation of the first ministry. It is therefore an invaluable account of development throughout the period told from experience but with a broad political perspective.

Secondary sources

Macleod RM **Anatomy of state medicine: concept and application** In Poynter FNL (ed). Medicine and science in the 1860s. London, Wellcome Historical Medical Library, 1968. *Idem* **The frustration of state medicine, 1880–1889** In Medical History. 11, 1967. These two articles provide an overview of the rise and decline of the concept and practice of state medicine based primarily in central government administration.

Rosen George **From medical police to social medicine. Essays on the history of health care** New York, Science History

Publications, 1974. Rosen traces the origins of 19th and 20th century concepts of social medicine from the date of the work of JP Frank, in the system of German cameralism.

THE CONTROVERSY ON THE NATURE OF DISEASE

Primary sources (listed chronologically)

Smith TS **A treatise on fever** London, Longman, 1830. The definitive English text on the official anti-contagionist orthodoxy of disease.

Snow John **On the mode of communication of cholera** London, John Churchill, 1855. The ideas which challenged the orthodoxy of the Chadwickian era and made out the case for the water-borne nature of cholera.

Parkes Edmund A **A manual of practical hygiene** London, John Churchill, 1864. The first English text book on public hygiene which provided a model for future publications by other authors. The revised editions (3rd 1869, 4th 1874) display Parkes' changing concept of disease.

Secondary sources

Ackerknecht Edwin **Anti-contagionism between 1821–1867** Bulletin of the History of Medicine, 22, 1948, pp 562–93. Ackerknecht wrote a crucial article about the disease controversy in the early 19th century which is still being addressed.

Bulloch W **History of bacteriology** London, Oxford University Press, 1938. Bulloch's work continues to be an extremely useful reference source.

Pelling Margaret **Cholera, fever and English medicine 1825–1865** London, Oxford University Press, 1978. Pelling clearly demonstrates the interaction of politics and science in the practice of medicine and public health during the period, through a critique of epidemiology.

THE HISTORY OF NATIONAL HEALTH AND COMMUNITY MEDICINE

Bruce Maurice **The coming of the welfare state** London, Batsford, 1965. Sound political history of the conflicting ideas and events which preceded the development of a welfare economy in Britain.

Gilbert Bentley B **The evolution of national insurance in Great Britain** London, Michael Joseph, 1966. History of the scheme, with a detailed account of the medical side, and its execution.

Francis Huw **Towards community medicine: the British experience**; also Warren MD **Specialist training in community medicine** Both in Bennett AE (ed). Recent advances in community medicine 1. Edinburgh, Churchill Livingstone, 1978. These essays on the history of the structure of service and specialist training in health care for community provide an overview of the transition from public health to community medicine.

Hodgkinson Ruth **The origins of the National Health Service: the medical services of the new Poor Law 1834–1871** London, Wellcome Historical Medical Library, 1967. This remains the most comprehensive work on the medical services of the new Poor Law, an important feature of the prehistory of the National Health Service.

Jefferys Margot **The transition from public health to community medicine** Bulletin of the Society for the Social History of Medicine, 39, 1986. Sociological study of the process of change to community medicine and its consequences.

Webster Charles **Problems of health care: the National Health Service before 1957** London, HMSO, in press. The most important work in the field of studies written since the Second World War. The official historian of the National Health Service has had access to departmental and Cabinet records never before made available to scholars.

THE PEOPLE'S HEALTH

McKeown T **The modern rise of population** London, Edward Arnold, 1976. McKeown accounts for the rise of population levels since 1750 with improved standards of nutrition and the achievements of the public health movement.

Smith FB **The people's health 1830–1910** London, Croom Helm, 1979. The achievements and failures of health care provision are examined from the patient's point of view. He assesses the effects on the population of the period from infancy to old age.

JOURNALS AS A PRIMARY SOURCE

Public Health The official journal of the Society of Medical Officers of Health.

The Medical Officer Newsletter and communication vehicle for members of the profession, plus full-length articles.

The Lancet
British Medical Journal
The primary medical press.

The Journal of Preventive Medicine (formerly the Journal of State Medicine) The official journal of the Royal Institute of Hygiene.

The Journal of the Royal Sanitary Institute A publication largely concerned with sanitary engineering.

Transactions of the Epidemiology Society Many articles related to topics concerned with public health and preventive medicine.

APPENDICES

APPENDIX A

The forty-eight metropolitan medical officers of health

City of London	1855–1874	Henry Letheby
Balham	1855–1857	Francis Ward
Battersea	1855–1870	William Connor
Bermondsey	1855–1862	John Challice
Bethnal Green	1855–1863	S Pearce
Camberwell	1855–1894	JS Bristowe
Charlton	1855–1882	R Finch
Chelsea	1855–1884	AW Barclay
Clapham	1855–1883	J McDonough
Clerkenwell	1855–1895	JW Griffith
Eltham	1855–1893	David King Jnr
Fulham	1855–1876	FJ Burge
Greenwich	1855–1884	HN Pink
Hackney	1855–1891	John W Tripe
Hampstead	1855–1879	Charles FJ Lord
Holborn	1855–1895	Septimus Gibbon
Islington	1855–1871	E Ballard
Kensington	1855–1869	J Godrich
Lambeth	1855–1863	W Odling
Lee	1855–1885	JS Burton
Lewisham and Penge	1856–1884	FE Wilkinson
Limehouse	1855–1858	A Cleland
Mile End	1855–1866	JH Freeman
Paddington	1855–1867	J Burdon Sanderson
Poplar	1855–1877	SK Ellison
Poplar and Bow	1855–1866	T Ansell
Putney	1855–1875	RH Whiteman
Rotherhide	1855–1858	W Murdoch
St George-in-the-East	1855–1863	SR Pittard
St George-the-Martyr	1855–1860	W Rendle
St George,	1855–1867	CB Aldis
Hanover Square		R Druitt
St Giles	1855–1857	T Hunt
St James,		
Westminster	1855–1873	Edwin Lankester

St Luke, Middlesex	1855–1884	FW Pavy
St Martin-in-the-Fields	1855–1882	Lionel J Beale
St Mary, Newington	1855–1887	WT Iliff
St Marylebone	1856–1864	R Dundas Thomson
St Olave, Southwark	1855–1888	James N Vinen
St Pancras	1855–1868	Thomas Hillier
St Saviour, Southwark	1855–1891	R Bianchi
Shoreditch	1855–1872	R Barnes
Strand	1855–1892	C Evans
Streatham	1855–1857	A Browne
Tooting	1855–1857	W Chapman
Wandsworth	1855–1892	GE Nicholas
Westminster		
(St Margaret and St John)	1855–1893	B Holt
Whitechapel	1855–1880	J Liddle

178

APPENDIX B

The medical police of London

An anonymous article under this heading appeared in the *Journal of Public Health and Sanitary Review* in 1855. It contains the earliest suggestion for the formation of a society of medical officers of health.

By the provisions of the new Act for 'the better Local Management of the Metropolis,' a plan is presented by which the whole of the modern Babylon may be placed under constant scientific sanitary supervision. If properly carried out, this will in time become the leading feature of the Act, and will render London, which has long been, comparatively speaking, a healthy city, healthier than many of our small country towns noted for salubrity. It will, however, take some time for the due organization of the important corps who will henceforth become the sanitary police of London; for, in the first place, amongst the hosts of applicants for the duties of the sanitarian, it can scarcely fail to occur that some will be elected who are neither by taste nor by special education fully fitted for the duties implied; and, in the second place, the duties themselves have in a great degree to be learned and defined. If, however, the proper men are found for the position, the duties will follow in train as a matter of necessity. It is in the selection of officers, therefore, that the Municipal Councils and District Boards must be most careful ... The man who would represent fully the sanitary office requires, perhaps, more extended acquirements than belongs to the majority of men who follow scientific occupations. He should have a knowledge of practical chemistry; of the symptoms, causes, and treatment of disease; of physiology, or the laws of life; of pathology, or the laws of morbid action; of forensic medicine, or the connection that exists between the science of medicine and the law; of various kinds, bearing on sewerage, house-building, street-cleansing, and water-supply; of meteorology, or the effects of climate, weather, and atmospheric influences on the body; of the physical characters or dynamics of the atmosphere; of ventilation; of statistics of life and mortality; of the literature of epidemics, and of all sanitary improvements. Lastly, he should possess sound logical faculties, so that in dealing with facts and opinions he may neither mistake coincidences for causes, nor build up great theories on insignificant data, nor from great facts deduce absurd conclusions. There is here, it is true, a high standard of qualification; and it may be difficult to find anyone who shall come up to it in all its fulness. But he who approaches it nearest is most fit for the place in question; and for him who bears its measurement best it is the duty of each municipal board to seek earnestly.

It has been observed that, if the proper men are elected for the duties of officers of health, London will soon have the best Council of Health that could be devised, and that the State might so organize this council, and so place itself in connection with it, as to obtain the advice and assistance of a truly scientific body in all national emergencies when sanitary advice is required. This would indeed be a grand ultimatum; but we hope that, as soon as the elections have taken place, the officers elected will spontaneously organize themselves into an independent association for the advancement of sanitary science ... A yearly report of the sanitary state of all London, drawn up by scientific and independent men, would in twenty years throw more light on the general causes of disease and on the principles of prevention than all the stray medical writings on these subjects which have appeared since the days of Hippocrates.

APPENDIX C

The first London University syllabus for the DPH, 1887

The London University syllabus for the DPH as approved and recognised by the General Medical Council on 21 February 1887 for purposes of registration in the Medical Registrar under section 21 of the Medical Act 1886.

I. CHEMISTRY AND MICROSCOPY, as regards the examination of Air, Water, and Food.

II. METEOROLOGY, as regards general knowledge of Meteorological Conditions, and the reading and correction of Instruments.

III. GEOLOGY, as regards general knowledge of Rocks, their conformation and chemical composition, and their relation to underground Water, and to Drainage and sources of Water-supply.

IV. PHYSICS AND SANITARY APPARATUS. The laws of Heat, Mechanics, Pneumatics, Hydrostatics, and Hydraulics, in relation (for sanitary purposes) to the Construction of Dwellings, and to the Principles of Warming, Ventilation, Drainage, and Water-supply, and to forms of Apparatus for these and other sanitary uses; and the reading of Plans, Sections, Scales, &c. in regard of Sanitary Constructions and Appliances.

V. VITAL STATISTICS, as regards the methods employed for determining the Health of a Community; Birth-rate; Death-rate; Disease-rate; Life-tables; Duration and expectancy of Life. Present amount of Mortality at the various ages, and its causes, in different Classes and Communities. Practical statistics of Armies, Navies, Civil Professions, Asylums, Hospitals, Dispensaries, Lying-in Establishments, Prisons, Indoor and Out-door Paupers, Friendly Societies, Sick-Clubs, Medical and Surgical Practice, Towns.

VI. HYGIENE, including the Causation and Prevention of Disease; in which branch of examination reference shall be had to such matters as the following:—

Parentage, as influencing the individual expectation of Health, Temperaments; morbid diatheses; congenital diseases and malformations.

Effects of close interbreeding.

Special liabilities of the Health at particular Periods of Life. Physical regimen of different Ages.

Earth and Climate, and Changes of Season, in their bearing on the Health of Populations; Dampness of Soil; Malaria.

Conditions of healthy nourishment. – Dietaries and dietetic habits; stimulants and narcotics in popular use; dietetic privation, excesses, and errors, as respectively causing disease. Drinking-water, and the conditions which make water unfit for drinking. Adulterations of Food.

Conditions of healthy Lodgement. – Ventilation and Warming, and the removal of refuse-matters, in their respective relations to health. Filth as a cause of disease, Sanitary regimen of Towns and Villages. 'Nuisances' (as defined by law) with regard to the sanitary bearing and the removal of each. Trade-processes causing offensive effluvia. Common lodging-houses and tenement houses.

Conditions of healthy Activity. – Work, over-work, rest, and recreation. Occupations of different sorts in relation to the health of persons engaged in them; e.g., factory work in general; occupations which produce irritative lung disease; occupations which promote heart disease; occupations which deal with poisons &c.

Hygiene of particular Establishments and particular Classes of Population. Factories and Work-places; Schools; Workhouses; Asylums; Hospitals; Prisons.

Disease as distributed in England. – Classifications of disease for various purposes of medical inquiry. Excesses of particular diseases and injuries at particular places and at particular times. Particular Diseases, as regards their intimate nature, causation, and preventability:– e.g., Enteric Fever, Cholera, Typhus, Smallpox, Scarlatina, Diphtheria, Erysipelas, Pyaemia, Tubercular Diseases, Rheumatism, Ague, Cretinism, Ophthalmia, Porrigo, Venereal Diseases, Scurvy, Ergotism, Leprosy, Insanity.

Processes of Contagion in different diseases; incubation in each case. Particular dangers of infection; at schools, workplaces, &c.; and from laundries, dairies, &c.

Disinfectants, and establishments for Disinfection.
Quarantine.
Hospitals for Infectious Disease.
Conveyance of the Sick.
Vaccination. Existing knowledge as to its protectiveness.
Re-vaccination. Precautions which vaccination requires.
Arrangements for Public Vaccination in town and country.
Natural Cowpox.
Prostitution as regards the Public Health.
Diseases of Domestic Animals in relation to the Health
of Man. Rabies. Farcy and Glanders. Anthrax. Parasites,
especially Trichina and the Taeniadae. Aphtha. Tubercle.
Meat and milk of diseased animals.
Diseases of the Vegetable Kingdom and failures of vegetable
crops, in relation to the Health of Man. Famine-diseases.
Poisons in manufacture and commercial and domestic
use:– e.g., Arsenic, Lead, Phosphorus, Mercury. Poisoning
pigments.

VII. SANITARY LAW. The constitution and modes of procedure
of the respective Authorities in Sanitary Matters, together
with any existing Orders, Regulations, or Model By-laws of
the Local Government Board affecting the same. A general
acquaintance with the principal Statutes relating to Public
Health, including the following and subsequent Acts: – The
Public Health Act 1875. The Vaccination Acts. The Rivers
Pollution Prevention Act 1876. The Sale of Food and Drugs
Act 1875. The Acts relating to Artisans' Dwellings and
the Dwellings of the Poor. The Acts relating to Factories
and Work-places.

The Examination, which shall be both written and practical,
shall extend over four days, and shall be conducted in the following
order:–

WRITTEN EXAMINATION

Monday
  Morning, 10 to 1.   Hygiene
  Afternoon, 3 to 6.   Hygiene (continued).   Sanitary Law.
Tuesday
  Morning, 10 to 1.   Physics and Sanitary Apparatus.
  Afternoon, 3 to 6.   Vital Statistics. Geology.

PRACTICAL EXAMINATION

Wednesday, at 10 a.m.

Chemical and Microscopical Examination of Samples of Air, Water, and Food. Examination of articles of Dress and Decoration suspected of containing poison.

Thursday, at 10 a.m.

Meteorology; Sanitary Apparatus and Plans; Sanitary Reporting; Statistical Practice.

APPENDIX D

Qualifications in Public Health
as given in the Medical Register, 1887

Licensing Body	Title
Royal College of Physicians, London and	
Royal College of Surgeons, England	Diploma in Public Health
Royal College of Physicians, Edinburgh	Certificate of qualification in Public Health
King and Queens College of Physicians in Ireland	Diploma in State Medicine
Faculty of Physicians and Surgeons of Glasgow	Qualification in Public Health
Royal College of Surgeons in Ireland	Diploma in Public Health
University of Oxford	Certificate in Preventive Medicine and Public Health
University of Cambridge	Certificate in Sanitary Science Diploma in Public Health
University of Durham	Licence in Sanitary Science
University of London	Certificate in subjects relating to Public Health
University of Edinburgh	Bachelor and Doctor of Science in Department of Public Health
University of Glasgow	Qualification in Public Health
University of Dublin	Qualification in State Medicine
Royal University of Ireland	Diploma in Sanitary Science

'A lucubrating correspondent'

In 1894 *Public Health* published these two poems side by side,
giving two views of the medical officer of health. They had been
submitted by 'a lucubrating correspondent'.

A

Happy the man who, free
  from care,
Enscounced in easy office
  chair,
Before a kneehole table
  poses,
On an official bed of roses.
Permanent servant of the
  nation,
He gives whole time to sani-
  tation,
And ever grumbling at the
  pay,
Draws near enough three
  pounds a day.
For public health are all
  his labours,
He steals no cases from his
  neighbours,
Nor dreads the surgery bell's
  alarm,
But sleeps all night in
  healthy calm.
No diagnoses rack his brain;
Committees nag at him in
  vain;
No ratepayers' association
Can check his work of sani-
  tation.
Inspectors tremble at his
  nod,
A Sanitary Demi-God.

B

Look now at one whose
  cruel fate,
Condemns him to a meaner
  state,
Who once a year goes hat in
  hand,
To beg for what he should
  command.
Whose tenure's simply at the
  will
Of men who dare do evil
  still.
His salary a pittance mere,
Some ten or twenty pounds
  a year;
His office shared with his
  inspector,
Or even with the rate collec-
  tor:
Ill-paid, ignored, and mis-
  construed,
'Till were he with such gifts
  endued,
As made him M.O.H.
  indeed,
In such a post he'd ne'er
  succeed.

On this side Duty, on the
  other
His board, his practice, and
  less bother.
The L.G.B. may send in-
  spectors,
Yet prove his very worst
  protectors.
A thousand trifles him
  annoy,
Poor Sanitary Whipping
  Boy.

APPENDIX F

Local Government Board
Duties of the Medical Officer of Health

The following shall be the duties of a medical officer of health in respect of the sanitary district for which he is appointed; or if he shall be appointed for more than one district, or for part of a district, then in respect of each of such districts, or of such part:–

(1) He shall inform himself as far as practicable respecting all influences affecting or threatening to affect injuriously the public health within the district.

(2) He shall enquire into and ascertain by such means as are at his disposal the causes, origin, and distribution of diseases within the district, and ascertain to what extent the same have depended on conditions capable of removal or mitigation.

(3) He shall by inspection of the district, both systematically at certain periods and at intervals as occasion may require, keep himself informed of the conditions injurious to health existing therein.

(4) He shall be prepared to advise the sanitary authority on all matters affecting the health of the district, and on all sanitary points involved in the action of the sanitary authority; and in cases requiring it, he shall certify, for the guidance of the sanitary authority, or of the justices, as to any matter in respect of which the certificate of a medical officer of health or a medical practitioner is required as the basis or in aid of sanitary action.

(5) He shall advise the sanitary authority on any question relating to health involved in the framing and subsequent working of such by-laws and regulations as they may have power to make.

(6) On receiving information of the outbreak of any contagious, infectious, or epidemic disease of a dangerous character within the district, he shall visit the spot without delay and enquire into the causes and circumstances of such outbreak, and advise the persons competent to act as to the measures which may appear to him to be required to prevent the extension of the disease, and, so far as he may be lawfully authorised, assist in the execution of the same.

188

(7) On receiving information from the inspector of nuisances that his intervention is required in consequence of the existence of any nuisance injurious to health, or of any overcrowding in a house, he shall, as early as practicable, take such steps authorised by the statutes in that behalf as the circumstances of the case may justify and require.

(8) In any case in which it may appear to him to be necessary or advisable, or in which he shall be so directed by the sanitary authority, he shall himself inspect and examine any animal, carcase, meat, poultry, game, flesh, fish, fruit, vegetables, corn, bread, or flour, exposed for sale, or deposited for the purpose of sale or of preparation for sale and intended for the food of man, which is deemed to be diseased, or unsound, or unwholesome, or unfit for the food of man; and if he finds that such animal or article is diseased, or unsound, or unwholesome, or unfit for the food of man, he shall give such directions as may be necessary for causing the same to be seized, taken, and carried away, in order to be dealt with by a justice according to the provisions of the statutes applicable to the case.

(9) He shall perform all the duties imposed upon him by any by-laws and regulations of the sanitary authority, duly confirmed, in respect of any matter affecting the public health, and touching which they are authorised to frame by-laws and regulations.

(10) He shall enquire into any offensive process of trade carried on within the district, and report on the appropriate means for the prevention of any nuisance or injury to health therefrom.

(11) He shall attend at the office of the sanitary authority, or at some other appointed place, at such stated times as they may direct.

(12) He shall from time to time report, in writing, to the sanitary authority his proceedings, and the measures which may require to be adopted for the improvement or protection of the public health in the district. He shall in like manner report with respect to the sickness and mortality within the district, so far as he has been enabled to ascertain the same.

(13) He shall keep a book or books, to be provided by the sanitary authority, in which he shall make an entry of his visits, and notes of his observations and instructions thereon, and also the date and nature of applications made to him, the date and result of the action taken thereon, and of any action taken on previous

reports, and shall produce such book or books, whenever required, to the sanitary authority.

(14) He shall also prepare an annual report to be made to the end of December in each year, comprising tabular statements of the sickness and mortality within the district, classified according to diseases, ages, and localities, and a summary of the action taken during the year for preventing the spread of disease. The report shall also contain an account of the proceedings in which he has taken part or advised under the sanitary Acts, so far as such proceedings relate to conditions dangerous or injurious to health, and also an account of the supervision exercised by him, or on his advice, for sanitary purposes over places and houses that the sanitary authority has power to regulate, with the nature and results of any proceedings which may have been so required and taken in respect of the same during the year. It shall also record the action taken by him, or on his advice, during the year, in regard to offensive trades, bakehouses, and workshops.

(15) He shall give immediate information to the Local Government Board of any outbreak of dangerous epidemic diseases within the district, and shall transmit to the Board, on forms to be provided by them, a quarterly return of the sickness and deaths within the district, and also a copy of each annual and of any special report.

(16) In matters not specifically provided for in this order, he shall observe and execute, so far as the circumstances of the district may require, the instructions of the Local Government Board on the duties of medical officers of health, and all the lawful orders and directions of the sanitary authority applicable to his office.

(17) Whenever the Diseases' Prevention Act of 1855 is in force within the district, he shall observe the directions and regulations issued under that Act by the Local Government Board, so far as the same relate to or concern his office.

(18) Where more than one medical officer of health shall be appointed by a sanitary authority, such authority, with the approval of the Local Government Board, may either assign to each of the officers a portion of the district, or may distribute the duties of medical officer of health amongst such officers.

11 November 1872

APPENDIX G

Preparation of annual report, 1880

By an Order of the Local Government Board, dated March, 1880, Article 18, Section 14, it is prescribed, that every Medical Officer of Health shall –

'Prepare an Annual Report, to be made to the end of December in each year, comprising a summary of the action taken during the year for preventing the spread of disease, and an account of the sanitary state of his district generally, at the end of the year.

The Report shall also contain an account of the inquiries which he has made as to conditions injurious to health existing in his district, and of the proceedings in which he has taken part or advised under the Public Health Act, 1875, so far as such proceedings relate to those conditions.

Also an account of the supervision exercised by him, or on his advice, for sanitary purposes, over places and houses that the Sanitary Authority have power to regulate, with the nature and results of any proceedings which may have been so required and taken in respect of the same during the year.

It shall also record the action taken by him, or on his advice, during the year, in regard to offensive trades and to factories and workshops.

The report shall also contain tabular statements of the sickness and mortality within the district, classified according to diseases, ages, and localities.'

APPENDIX H

Chief medical officers and their predecessors

ENGLAND AND WALES

General Board of Health (1848–58)

From 1855, Sir John Simon

Privy Council (1858–71)

1858–71   Sir John Simon

Local Governmental Board (1871–1919)

1871–76   Sir John Simon (previously with the Privy Council and General Board of Health)
1876–79   Dr E C Seaton
1880–92   Sir George Buchanan
1892–99   Sir Richard Thorne Thorne
1900–08   Sir William Henry Power
1908–19   Sir Arthur Newsholme

Ministry of Health (1919–68)

1919–35   Sir George Newman
1935–40   Sir Arthur MacNalty
1940–50   Sir Wilson Jameson
1950–60   Sir John Charles
1960–68   Sir George Godber (continued as CMO to the DHSS)

Department of Health and Social Security (1968–)

1968–73   Sir George Godber
1973–84   Sir Henry Yellowlees
1984–   Sir Donald Acheson

Since 1969 there has been a separate CMO for Wales.

CHIEF MEDICAL OFFICERS, SCOTLAND

1929–32   Dr John Parlane Kinlock
1932–37   Dr James Law Brownlie
1937–41   Dr James M Mackintosh

1941–54   Sir Andrew Davidson
1954–64   Sir (Henry) Kenneth Cowan
1964–77   Sir John Howie Flint Brotherston
1977–85   Sir John James Andrew Reid
1985–   Dr Iain S MacDonald

CHIEF MEDICAL OFFICERS, WALES

1969–77   Dr R T Bevan
1977–   Dr G Crompton

APPENDIX I

Presidents of the Society of Medical Officers of Health (founded 1856)

1856–61	Sir John Simon	1912–13	EW Hope
1861–64	RD Thomson	1913–14	AK Chalmers
1864–72	R Druitt	1914–15	H Jones
1872–75	H Letheby	1915–16	FJ Allen
1875–77	G Buchanan	1916–17	Professor J Robertson
1877–79	T Stevenson		
1879–81	JS Bristowe	1917–18	C Saunders
1881–83	JW Tripe	1918–20	Professor H Kenwood (re-elected)
1883–85	TO Dudfield		
1885–86	WH Corfield	1920–21	Lt Col FE Freemantle MP
1886–88	A Mill		
1888–89	WH Corfield	1921–22	WJ Howarth
1889–91	HE Armstrong	1922–23	E Hill
1891–93	SF Murphy	1923–24	TWN Barlow
1893–94	WTG Woodforde	1924–25	RA Lyster
1894–95	SR Lovett	1925–26	GF Buchan
1895–96	F Vacher	1926–27	EH Snell
1896–97	GP Bate	1927–28	J Wheatley (died in office; Dr Snell re-elected)
1897–98	E Seaton		
1898–99	E Gwynn		
1899–1900	A Newsholme	1928–29	J Howard Jones
1900–01	JC McVail	1929–30	JJ Buchan
1901–02	AW Blyth	1930–31	Professor H Kerr OBE
1902–03	JS Cameron		
1903–04	J Groves	1931–32	C Killick Millard
1904–05	JFJ Sykes	1932–33	GH Pearce
1905–06	Sir Shirley F Murphy	1933–34	C Porter
1906–07	DS Davies	1934–35	R Veitch Clark
1907–08	G Reid	1935–36	WG Savage
1908–09	E Sargeant	1936–37	E Ward
1909–10	H Cooper-Pattin		(Tuberculosis officer, first president, except Lt Col Freemantle who was not an MOH)
1910–11	WG Willoughby		
1911–12	Professor A Bostock-Hill		
1912–13	EW Hope		

1937–38	J Fenton	1960–61	GWH Townsend
1938–39	EHT Nash	1961–62	Nora I Wattie
1939–41	FTH Wood (re-elected)	1962–63	E Hughes
		1963–64	HM Cohen
1941–42	Sir Alexander Macgregor	1964–65	Dorothy F Egan
		1965–66	J Maddison
1942–43	C Banks	1966–67	JB Tilley
1943–44	RHH Jolly	1967–68	RCM Pearson
1944–45	RMF Picken	1968–69	Professor RC Wofinden
1945–46	Professor J Johnstone Jarvis	1969–70	JBS Morgan
1946–47	Sir Allen Daley	1970–71	JR Preston
1947–48	F Hall	1971–72	WG Harding
1948–49	Professor RH Parry	1972–73	JL Gilloran

1937–38	J Fenton
1938–39	EHT Nash
1939–41	FTH Wood (re-elected)
1941–42	Sir Alexander Macgregor
1942–43	C Banks
1943–44	RHH Jolly
1944–45	RMF Picken
1945–46	Professor J Johnstone Jarvis
1946–47	Sir Allen Daley
1947–48	F Hall
1948–49	Professor RH Parry
1949–50	HC Maurice Williams
1950–51	J McT Gibson
1951–52	WG Clark
1952–53	A Topping
1953–54	C Metcalfe-Brown
1954–55	Jean M Mackintosh (first woman president)
1955–56	CF White
1956–57	JD Kershaw
1957–58	HD Chalke
1958–59	JA Stirling
1959–60	J Stevenson Logan

1960–61	GWH Townsend
1961–62	Nora I Wattie
1962–63	E Hughes
1963–64	HM Cohen
1964–65	Dorothy F Egan
1965–66	J Maddison
1966–67	JB Tilley
1967–68	RCM Pearson
1968–69	Professor RC Wofinden
1969–70	JBS Morgan
1970–71	JR Preston
1971–72	WG Harding
1972–73	JL Gilloran

Name changed to Society of Community Medicine

1973–74	MA Charrett
1974–75	AM Nelson
1975–77	H Binysh (re-elected)
1977–78	WT Orton
1978–79	JH Whittles
1979–80	JS Robertson
1980–81	DK MacTaggart
1981–82	C Simpson-Smith
1982–83	P Beynon
1983–84	PA Gardner
1984–85	L McMurdo

APPENDIX J

Presidents, Faculty of Community Medicine of the Royal Colleges of Physicians (founded 1972)

1972–75	AL Cochrane
1975–78	WG Harding
1978–81	Sir John Brotherston
1981–86	E Alwyn Smith

APPENDIX K

Deans of the London School of Hygiene and Tropical Medicine

1928–31	Dr Andrew Balfour (Director)
1931–40	Sir Wilson Jameson
1940–43	Brigadier GS Parkinson
1943–44	Professor Major Greenwood
1944–49	Professor James Mackintosh
1949–55	Dr Andrew Topping
1955–57	Sir Austin Bradford Hill
1957–60	Sir James Kilpatrick
1960–70	Dr ETC Spooner
1970–	Dr CE Gordon Smith

APPENDIX L

Professors and Directors of Department of Public Health/Community Health, London School of Hygiene and Tropical Medicine

1929–40   Sir Wilson Jameson (was professor designate 1929–31)
1944–56   James Mackintosh
1956–66   Stanley Walton GM
1966–78   JN Morris
1978–80   Michael Warren
1982*–   Patrick JS Hamilton

---

* From 1980–82 Rosemary Rue, was director, on part-time secondment from her post as Regional Medical Officer, Oxford Regional Health Authority; and, between July and September 1982, Stuart Morrison was temporary director.

APPENDIX M

Professors of Public Health/Community Medicine, University of Edinburgh

1898–1924   Charles H Stewart
1925–44   Brevet Colonel Percy S Lelean
1944–55   Brigadier Francis AE Crew
1955–64   Sir John HF Brotherston
1964–75   Stuart L Morrison
1977*–80   Sir John HF Brotherston
1983**–   William Michael Garraway

---

* 1975–77   Donald Cameron Acting Head
**1980–83   CM Una Maclean Acting Head

APPENDIX N

List of publications of Dr SPW Chave

With H Williams Smith. A rapid screening test for use in the bacteriological examination of faeces. Monthly Bulletin of the Ministry of Health and Public Health Laboratory Service, 1949, pp 240–44.

Exhibition projects in public health teaching. Medical and Biological Illustration, 1956, VI, 1, pp 4–8.

With JHF Brotherston and others. General practice on a new housing estate. British Journal of Preventive and Social Medicine, 1956, 10, pp 200–7.

Bringing history to life: the preparation of an exhibition on the medical officer of health. Medical Officer, 1956, 2527, pp 389–90.

Minds and machines. The Listener, 1957, LVII, 1452, p 157.

Rivers: the ecologist's point of view. The River Boards Association Year Book, 1957.

With FM Martin and JHF Brotherston. Incidence of neurosis in a new housing estate. British Journal of Preventive and Social Medicine, 1957, 11, 4, pp 196–202.

Henry Whitehead and cholera in Broad Street. Medical History, 1958, II, 2, pp 92–108.

John Snow: the Broad Street pump and after. Medical Officer, 1958, 99, pp 347–9.

Producing an exhibition: an exercise in public health teaching. Health Education Journal, 1959, XVII, 2, pp 94–7.

The smoking habits of school children. Report of a study group of the Public Health Department, London School of Hygiene and Tropical Medicine. British Journal of Preventive and Social Medicine, 1959, 13, 1, pp 1–4.

Ionising radiations: introduction to radiation. Journal for Industrial Nurses, 1961, XIII, 1, pp 1–8.

A study of the mentally handicapped child. Report of a study group at the London School of Hygiene and Tropical Medicine. National Society for Mentally Handicapped Children, 1962.

The case for fluoridation. Mother and Child, 1963, 33, 12, pp 220–1.

Fluoridation in Watford: a survey of public opinion. Medical Officer, 1963, 110, pp 381–2.

With Lord Taylor. Mental health and environment. London, Longmans, Green & Company Ltd, 1964.

With Beryl Jones, BT Williams and a group of DPH students. The health educator. Medical Officer, 1964, 112, pp 205–7.

The creation of communities. Housing in human terms. Town and Country Planning, 1966, 34, 377–9.

Mental health in Harlow New Town. Journal of Psychosomatic Research, 1966, 10, pp 38–44.

Mental health today: an appraisal. Health Education Journal, 1967, 26, pp 153–6.

Measurements in health education. Journal of the Institute of Health Education, 1970, 8, 3, pp 68–76.

Opening address to the 1972 annual conference on public health aspects of the Victorian period. Society for the Social History of Medicine Bulletin No 8, 1972, pp 4–7.

With JN Morris, C Adam, C Sirey, L Epstein and DJ Sheehan. Vigorous exercise in leisure-time and the incidence of coronary heart disease. The Lancet, 1973, I, pp 333–9.

The medical officer of health, 1848–1973. The Society for the Social History of Medicine Bulletin No 12, 1973, pp 2–4.

The medical officer of health, 1847–1974; the formative years. Proceedings of the Royal Society of Medicine, 1974, 67, pp 1243–7.

The Royal Society of Health in the USSR: some personal impressions. Royal Society of Health Journal, 1977, 97, p 91.

The evolution of community medicine. Society for the Social History of Medicine Bulletin No 16, 1975, 4, pp 14–15.

With G Chamberlain. Antenatal education. Community Health, 1977, 89, pp 11–16.

With JN Morris, Susan Moss and AM Semmence. Vigorous exercise in leisure time and the death rate: a study of male civil servants. Journal of Epidemiology and Community Health, 1978, 32, 4, 239–43.

The rise and fall of the medical officer of health. The Monckton Copeman Lecture, the Worshipful Society of Apothecaries, 5 February 1979. Community Medicine, 1980, 2, pp 36–45.

With JN Morris, MG Everitt, R Pollard and AM Semmence. Vigorous exercise in leisure-time: protection against coronary heart disease. The Lancet, 1980, II, pp 1207–10.

Duncan of Liverpool – and some lessons for today. The Duncan Memorial Lecture. Community Medicine, 1984, 6, pp 61–71.

The origins and development of public health. In WW Holland *et al* (eds). Oxford Textbook of Public Health 1. Oxford, Oxford University Press, 1984, pp 3–19.

The School through fifty years: some personal reflections. London School of Hygiene and Tropical Medicine, 1976. MSS collection.

War diary. London, Imperial War Museum. MSS collection.